Assessment Tests
for
Higher
Chemistry

D A Buchanan
(Moray House Institute,
Edinburgh University)

J R Melrose
(Lenzie Academy, Lenzie, Glasgow)

Published by
Chemcord
Inch Keith
East Kilbride
Glasgow

ISBN   9 781870 570688

Printed by Bell and Bain Ltd, Glasgow

Contents

Note to teachers / lecturers

The tests are specifically designed to pin-point learning difficulties and to check students' understanding of the work covered in the Higher Chemistry course. The tests have been used over a number of years and found to be an invaluable aid to learning.

While the tests can be administered to the whole class, it is suggested that they can be more effectively used by students working at their own pace in class, during self-study time in school or as homework. The information from the results of the tests can be used to help students to plan revision. The test results can also be used by teachers / lecturers who are interested in assessing individual or class difficulties.

Each test is, by and large, independent of the others and consequently the tests can be used to fit almost any teaching order.

The variation in length of the tests is a reflection of the different kinds of question which are associated with a particular area of content. Consequently, different allocations of time are required.

Acknowledgement

A number of questions in the tests come from, or have evolved from, questions used in the SCE examinations. The publisher wishes to thank the Scottish Qualifications Authority for permission to use examination questions in these ways.

Test 1.1   Following the course of a reaction

In questions 1 to 6 decide whether each of the statements is

A. TRUE   **B.** FALSE.

1. The unit for average rate of reaction could be mol l⁻¹ s⁻¹. A

2. The unit for average rate of reaction could be cm³ s⁻¹. A

3. The unit for average rate of reaction could be mol l⁻¹. B

4. The unit for average rate of reaction could be g s⁻¹. A

5. The unit for average rate of reaction could be g l⁻¹. B

6. For a fixed change in concentration of a reactant, the shorter the time taken, the faster the rate of reaction. ̶B̶ A

7. The rate of a reaction is likely to be fastest nearer the end of the reaction. B

8. For some reactions, the reaction rate can double for every temperature rise of ten centigrade degrees. ̶B̶ A

Questions 9 to 11 refer to the graph which shows data obtained from the reaction of zinc with hydrochloric acid.

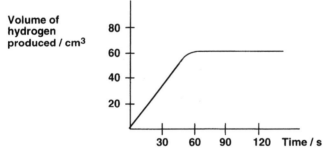

9. What was the total volume of hydrogen produced in the reaction? C

    A. 20 cm³   **B.** 40 cm³   **C.** 60 cm³   **D.** 80 cm³

10. How long did it take for the reaction to go to completion? B

    A. 30 s   **B.** 60 s   **C.** 90 s   **D.** 120 s

11. What was the average rate at which hydrogen was produced, in cm³ s⁻¹, in the first 30 s? A

    A. 1.2   **B.** 2.4   **C.** 3.6   **D.** 4.8

Questions 12 to 14 refer to the graph which shows how the concentration of a reactant in a reaction varied with time.

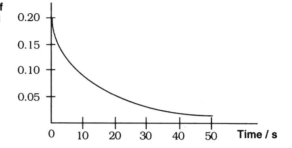

12. What was the initial concentration, in mol l^{-1}, of the reactant?

    A. 0.05   **B.** 0.10   **C.** 0.15   **D.** 0.20

13. What was the average rate at which the reactant was used up, in mol l^{-1} s^{-1}, in the first 20 s?

    A. 0.0025   **B.** 0.0050   **C.** 0.0075   **D.** 0.0150

14. What was the average rate at which the reactant was used up, in mol l^{-1} s^{-1}, in the period 20 s to 40 s?

    A. 0.00050   **B.** 0.00125   **C.** 0.00250   **D.** 0.01250

Test 1.2

Rate of reactions (i)

In questions 1 to 12 decide whether each of the statements is

A. TRUE   **B.** FALSE.

1. Increasing the temperature increases the rate of reaction.

2. Lumps of calcium carbonate react faster with acid than calcium carbonate powder.

3. A dilute acid usually reacts faster than a concentrated acid.

4. Milk is more likely to turn sour at 0 °C than at 10 °C.

5. Small potatoes take longer to cook than large potatoes.

6. Plants grow faster in warm weather than in cold weather.

7. Compared with coal dust, lumps of coal burn very rapidly.

8. Acetylene burns less rapidly in pure oxygen than in air.

9. Chips cook faster in oil at 300 °C than in oil at 200 °C.

10. Reactions involving gases go faster when the pressure is increased.

11. One mole of hydrogen gas reacts with one mole of iodine vapour.
    After **t** seconds, 0.8 mol of hydrogen remains.

    What is the number of moles of hydrogen iodide formed at **t** seconds?

    A. 0.2   **B.** 0.4   **C.** 0.8   **D.** 1.6

12. The results of an experiment carried out at 19 °C involving the reaction between equal volumes of 0.5 mol l^{-1} nitric acid and sodium thiosulphate solution of different concentrations are shown.

Concentration of sodium thiosulphate solution/mol l^{-1}	0.5	0.25	0.125	0.064
Time for the appearance of sulphur/s	13	25	51	104

On the evidence of these results alone, which statement is correct?

A. The more concentrated the thiosulphate solution, the longer the time before the sulphur appears.

B. The more concentrated the nitric acid, the faster the reaction proceeds.

C. The more concentrated the thiosulphate solution, the faster the reaction proceeds.

D. The higher the temperature, the faster the reaction proceeds.

13. The continuous use of large extractor fans greatly reduces the possibility of an explosion in a flour mill.

    This is mainly because

    A. a build-up in the concentration of oxygen is prevented
    B. local temperature rises are prevented by the movement of air
    C. particles of flour suspended in the air are removed
    D. the slow accumulation of carbon monoxide is prevented.

14. Two identical samples of zinc are placed in open vessels. Excess of 2 mol l^{-1} sulphuric acid is added to one, and excess of 1 mol l^{-1} sulphuric acid is added to the other. All other conditions are the same.

    Which of the following is the same for the two samples?

    A. the mass lost from the vessels
    B. the total time for the reaction
    C. the initial reaction rate
    D. the average rate of evolution of gas

15. During the addition of magnesium to an excess of dilute hydrochloric acid, each of the following was measured and plotted against time on a graph.

    A. the temperature of the solution
    B. the volume of hydrogen produced
    C. the pH of the solution
    D. the concentration of the solution

    If the reaction was completed in 5 minutes, which of the above was measured to give the graph?

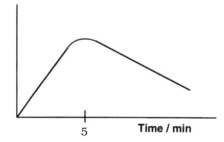

16. Which graph could apply to the following reaction?

$$S_2O_3{}^{2-}(aq) \quad + \quad 2H^+(aq) \quad \rightarrow \quad H_2O(l) \quad + \quad SO_2(g) \quad + \quad S(s)$$

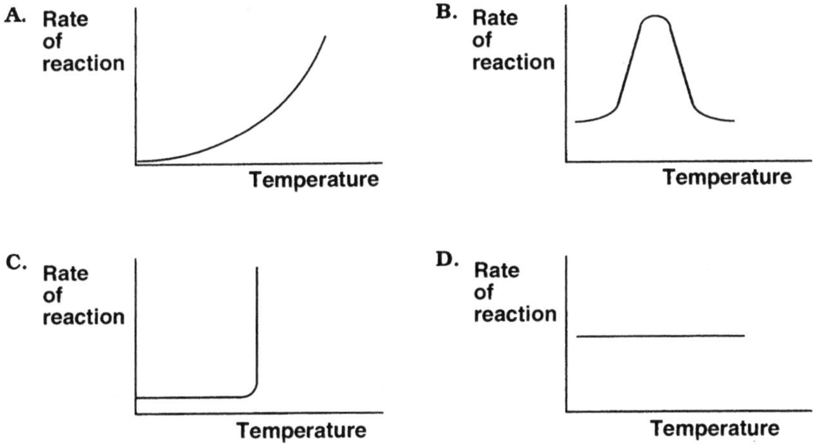

A. Rate
of
reaction

Temperature

B. Rate
of
reaction

Temperature

C. Rate
of
reaction

Temperature

D. Rate
of
reaction

Temperature

In questions 1 to 10 decide whether each of the statements is

A.   TRUE   **B.**   FALSE.

1. A catalyst can speed up the rate of a reaction.

2. A catalyst can be recovered chemically unchanged at the end of reaction.

3. A catalyst plays no part in a chemical reaction.

4. A catalyst provides an alternative route to the products.

5. A catalyst lowers the energy which molecules need for successful collisions.

6. A catalyst provides energy so that more molecules have successful collisions.

7. A catalyst forms bonds with reacting molecules.

8. The surface activity of a heterogeneous catalyst can be increased by poisoning.

9. The renewal of a catalyst involves removal of unwanted impurity on the surface.

10. Cars with catalytic convertors only use 'lead free' petrol.

In questions 11 to 14 decide whether the catalyst is an example of

A.   a homogeneous catalyst   **B.**   a heterogeneous catalyst.

11. platinum in the complete combustion of hydrocarbons and carbon monoxide in car exhaust systems

12. aqueous cobalt ions in the reaction between an aqueous solution of Rochelle salt and hydrogen peroxide solution

13. iron in the Haber Process

14. nickel in the hydrogenation of unsaturated oils to saturated fats

Test 1.4 Collision theory and activation energy

In questions 1 to 7 decide whether each of the statements is

A. TRUE   **B.** FALSE.

1. The collision theory can be used to explain the effects of concentration on reaction rates.

2. The collision theory can be used to explain the effects of temperature on reaction rates.

3. The activation energy is the minimum kinetic energy required by colliding particles before reaction will occur.

4. Energy distribution diagrams can be used to explain the effect of changing temperature on the kinetic energy of particles.

5. The effect of temperature on reaction rates can be explained in terms of an increase in the number of particles with energy greater than the activation energy.

6. The effect of temperature on reaction rates can be explained in terms of an increase in the surface area of particles.

7. With some chemical reactions, light can be used to increase the number of particles with energy greater than the activation energy.

8. For any chemical the temperature is measure of

    A. the average kinetic energy of the particles which react
    B. the average kinetic energy of all the particles
    C. the activation energy
    D. the minimum kinetic energy required before reaction occurs.

9. The graph opposite shows the distribution of kinetic energies of the molecules in a sample of gas.

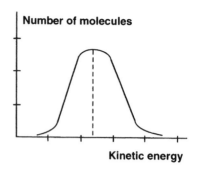

Which graph would show the kinetic energies of the molecules when the sample is cooled by 10 °C?

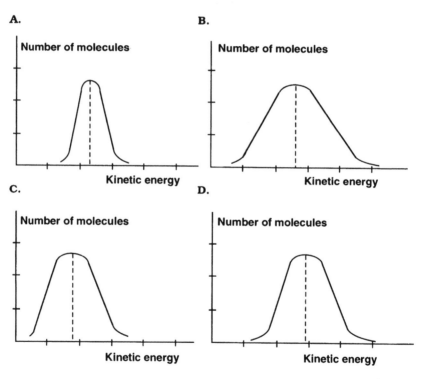

A.

B.

C.

D.

1. The graph shows the data obtained from three reactions of zinc with an excess of 2 mol l⁻¹ hydrochloric acid.

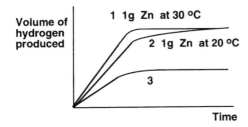

Which statement is true?

A. Increasing the temperature increases the total mass of hydrogen produced.

B. Increasing the temperature has no effect on the initial rate of reaction.

C. Curve **3** would be obtained with 1 g of zinc at 10 ^{0}C.

D. Curve **3** would be obtained with 0.5 g of zinc at 20 ^{0}C.

Questions 2 and 3 refer to the graph which shows the reactions of three metals with excess of 2 mol l⁻¹ hydrochloric acid.

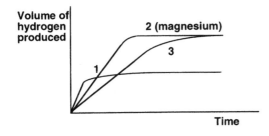

2. Which metal is likely to produce curve 1?

    A. lithium   **B.** aluminium   **C.** zinc   **D.** copper

3. Which metal is likely to produce curve 3?

    A. lithium   **B.** aluminium   **C.** zinc   **D.** copper

Questions 4 to 9 refer to the graphs which show data obtained from reactions of hydrochloric acid.

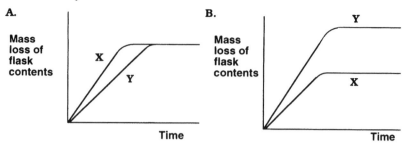

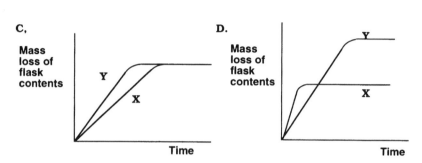

Which graph shows the data likely to be obtained from each of the pairs of reactions?

Contents of flask **X**

Contents of flask **Y**

4. 10 g chalk lumps (excess)
    50 cm^3 of 1 mol l^{-1} HCl(aq)
    20 °C

    10 g chalk powder (excess)
    50 cm^3 of 1 mol l^{-1} HCl(aq)
    20 °C

5. 4 cm magnesium ribbon
    50 cm^3 of 2 mol l^{-1} HCl(aq) (excess)
    20 °C

    4 cm magnesium ribbon
    50 cm^3 of 1 mol l^{-1} HCl(aq) (excess)
    20 °C

6. 10 g chalk (excess)
    50 cm^3 of 0.1 mol l^{-1} HCl(aq)
    20 °C

    10 g chalk (excess)
    50 cm^3 of 0.2 mol l^{-1} HCl(aq)
    20 °C

7. 4 cm magnesium ribbon
    50 cm³ of 2 mol l⁻¹ HCl(aq) (excess)
    20 °C

    8 cm magnesium ribbon
    50 cm³ of 1 mol l⁻¹ HCl(aq) (excess)
    20 °C

8. 2 g zinc (excess)
    50 cm³ of 1 mol l⁻¹ HCl(aq)
    20 °C with catalyst

    2 g zinc (excess)
    50 cm³ of 1 mol l⁻¹ HCl(aq)
    20 °C without catalyst

9. 2 g zinc (excess)
    50 cm³ of 1 mol l⁻¹ HCl(aq)
    20 °C

    2 g zinc (excess)
    50 cm³ of 1 mol l⁻¹ HCl(aq)
    40 °C

10. When copper carbonate reacts with excess acid, carbon dioxide is
    produced.
    The curves shown were obtained under two different conditions.

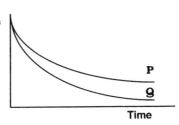

    The change from **P** to **Q** can be brought
    about by

    A. decreasing the concentration
    of the acid

    B. decreasing the mass of copper
    carbonate

    C. decreasing the particle size of
    the copper carbonate

    D. decreasing the temperature

11. The course of the reaction between
    magnesite (magnesium carbonate)
    and dilute hydrochloric acid was
    followed by determining the mass
    of the reaction vessel and contents
    as carbon dioxide was evolved.
    The curves shown were obtained under
    two different conditions.

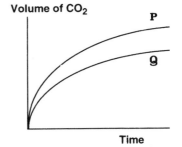

    The change from **P** to **Q** can be brought about by

    A. decreasing the concentration of the acid
    B. increasing the temperature of the reactants
    C. increasing the particle size of the magnesite
    D. decreasing the volume of the acid.

12. The graph opposite shows the volume of hydrogen given off against time when an excess of magnesium ribbon is added to 100 cm³ of hydrochloric acid, concentration 1 mol l⁻¹, at 30 °C.

Volume of H₂

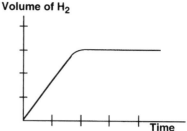

Which graph would show the volume of hydrogen given off when an excess of magnesium ribbon is added to 50 cm³ of hydrochloric acid of the same concentration at 20 °C?

A.

B.

C.

D.

13. Excess zinc was added to 100 cm³ of hydrochloric acid, concentration 1 mol l⁻¹.
Curve **1** refers to this reaction.

Volume of hydrogen produced

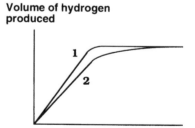

Curve **2** could be for

   A. excess zinc reacting with 100 cm³ of hydrochloric acid, concentration 2 mol l⁻¹

   B. excess zinc reacting with 100 cm³ of sulphuric acid, concentration 1 mol l⁻¹

   C. excess zinc reacting with 100 cm³ of ethanoic acid, concentration 1 mol l⁻¹

   D. excess magnesium reacting with 100 cm³ hydrochloric acid, concentration 1 mol l⁻¹.

Questions 1 to 5 refer to reactions of metals.

For each of the reactions decide whether

A.   reactant 1 is in excess   **B.**   reactant 2 is in excess
C.   neither is in excess.

1. Reactant 1 : 2.43 g of magnesium
    Reactant 2 : 100 cm^3 of hydrochloric acid, concentration 0.2 mol l^{-1}

2. Reactant 1 : 0.654 g of zinc
    Reactant 2 : 25 cm^3 of copper(II) sulphate solution, concentration 1 mol l^{-1}

3. Reactant 1 : 2.43 g of magnesium
    Reactant 2 : 50 cm^3 of sulphuric acid, concentration 2 mol l^{-1}

4. Reactant 1 : 6.35 g of copper
    Reactant 2 : 100 cm^3 of silver nitrate solution, concentration 2 mol l^{-1}

5. Reactant 1 : 2.43 g of magnesium
    Reactant 2 : 100 cm^3 of hydrochloric acid, concentration 1 mol l^{-1}

6. Hydrochloric acid reacts with magnesium.

    $$Mg_{(s)} \; + \; 2H^+_{(aq)} \; \rightarrow \; Mg^{2+}_{(aq)} \; + \; H_{2(g)}$$

    What is the minimum volume, in cm^3, of acid, concentration 4 mol l^{-1},
    required to react with 0.1 mol of metal?

    A.   25   **B.**   50   **C.**   100   **D.**   200

7. 0.243 g of magnesium is added to 100 cm^3 of hydrochloric acid,
    concentration 1 mol l^{-1}.

    How much hydrogen, in moles, is produced?

    A.   0.01   **B.**   0.02   **C.** 0.1   **D.**   0.2

8. 5 g copper powder is added to silver nitrate solution.   After some time the
    powder remaining is filtered off, washed with water and dried.

    The mass of the powder will be

    A.   more than 5 g   **B.**   equal to 5 g
    C.   less than 5 g   **D.**   unable to be calculated.

9. Copper carbonate is produced in the reaction of solutions of copper(II) sulphate and sodium carbonate, both of the same concentration.

$$Na_2CO_3(aq) + CuSO_4(aq) \rightarrow CuCO_3(s) + Na_2SO_4(aq)$$

Which mixture would give the greatest mass of precipitate?

A. 1.5 cm^3 of $Na_2CO_3(aq)$ + 0.5 cm^3 of $CuSO_4(aq)$

B. 0.5 cm^3 of $Na_2CO_3(aq)$ + 1.5 cm^3 of $CuSO_4(aq)$

C. 1.0 cm^3 of $Na_2CO_3(aq)$ + 1.0 cm^3 of $CuSO_4(aq)$

D. 2.0 cm^3 of $Na_2CO_3(aq)$ + 0.5 cm^3 of $CuSO_4(aq)$

10. How much hydrogen would be released by placing 6.54 g of zinc in 200 cm^3 of hydrochloric acid, concentration 1 mol l^{-1}?

A.   0.2 mol   B.   just over 0.2 mol
C.   0.1 mol   D.   just over 0.1 mol

Questions 11 to 14 refer to the addition of 2.43 g of magnesium to 250 cm^3 of copper(II) sulphate solution, concentration 2 mol l^{-1}.

Decide whether each of the staements is

A.   TRUE   B.   FALSE.

11. All of the magnesium reacts.

12. 0.025 mol of copper ions react.

13. 6.35 g of copper is displaced.

14. 0.25 mol of magnesium reacts.

Questions 15 to 18 refer to the addition of 63.5 g of copper to 1 litre of silver nitrate solution, concentration 1 mol l^{-1}.

Decide whether each of the staements is

A.   TRUE   B.   FALSE.

15. The resulting solution is colourless.

16. All the copper dissolves.

17. 63.5 g of silver is formed.

18. 1 mol of silver is formed.

Test 1.7

1. What types of changes cause heat to be released to the surroundings?

   A. exothermic   **B.** endothermic

2. What types of changes cause heat to be taken in from the surroundings?

   A. exothermic   **B.** endothermic

3. The enthalpy change for a reaction is the energy difference between which of the following?

   A. reactants and activated complex
   B. products and activated complex
   C. reactants and products

4. For exothermic reactions, the enthalpy change has a

   A. a negative value   **B.** a positive value.

5. For endothermic reactions, the enthalpy change has a

   A. a positive value   **B.** a negative value.

6. The activation energy for a forward reaction is the energy difference between

   A. the reactants and activated complex
   B. the products and activated complex
   C. the reactants and products.

7. In providing an alternative pathway for a reaction, a catalyst

   A. decreases the activation energy
   B. increases the activation energy.

Questions 8 to 10 refer to the energy diagram.

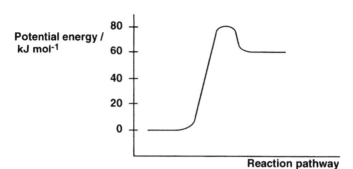

8. What is the enthalpy change, in kJ mol⁻¹, for the forward reaction?

A.	-60	B.	-20
C.	+60	D.	+80

9. What is the activation energy, in kJ mol⁻¹, for the forward reaction?

A.	20	B.	60
C.	40	D.	80

10. What is the activation energy, in kJ mol⁻¹, for the reverse reaction?

A.	20	B.	60
C.	40	D.	80

11.

The energy of activation for the forward reaction is given by

A.	Y	B.	Z - X
C.	Y - X	D.	Y - Z.

Questions 12 to 14 refer to the energy diagrams.

A.

Potential energy /
kJ mol⁻¹

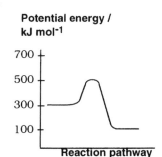

B.

Potential energy /
kJ mol⁻¹

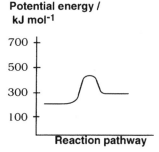

C.

Potential energy /
kJ mol⁻¹

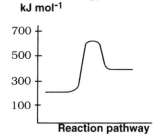

D.

Potential energy /
kJ mol⁻¹

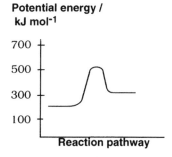

12. Which diagram represents the catalysed version of the reaction in diagram **D**?

13. Which diagram represents the forward reaction with the highest energy of activation?

14. Which diagram represents the forward reaction with an enthalpy change of -200 kJ mol⁻¹?

15. The energy diagram for the reaction

$$CO_{(g)} + NO_{2(g)} \rightarrow CO_{2(g)} + NO_{(g)}$$

is shown.

What is the enthalpy change, in kJ mol⁻¹, for the reverse reaction?

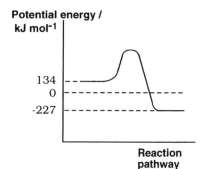

   A. +361
   B. -93
   C. -227
   D. -361

16.

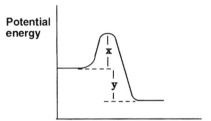

Reaction pathway

The activation energy for the reverse reaction can be represented by

A. **x**

B. **y**

C. **x + y**

D. **x - y**.

17. Which reaction should be most easily reversed?

A. Potential energy

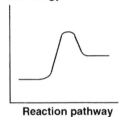

Reaction pathway

B. Potential energy

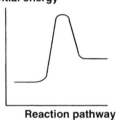

Reaction pathway

C. Potential energy

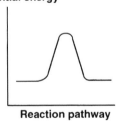

Reaction pathway

D. Potential energy

Reaction pathway

18. **Potential energy**   **Potential energy**

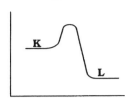 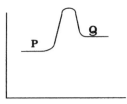

Reaction pathway   **Reaction pathway**

Which reaction has the greatest activation energy?

A. K → L   B. L → K
C. P → Q   D. Q → P

19. The unbroken line and the broken line represent the same reaction under different conditions.

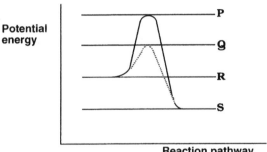

Reaction pathway

Which interval represents the enthalpy of the reaction?

A. RP   B. PS
C. RS   D. QS

20. Which of the following correctly represents the activation energy (Ea) and the enthalpy change (ΔH) for the forward reaction?

Potential energy

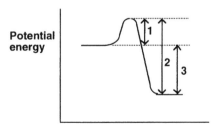

	Ea	ΔH
A.	2	3
B.	1	2
C.	1	3
D.	2	1

Reaction pathway

21. For the reaction $H_2(g)$ + $I_2(g)$ $\rightleftharpoons$ $2HI(g)$

the activation energy for the forward reaction is 181.5 kJ mol^{-1} and for the reverse reaction is 192.8 kJ mol^{-1}.

What is the enthalpy of formation, in kJ mol^{-1}, of $2HI(g)$?

A. +11.3   **B.** -11.3   **C.** +374.3   **D.** -374.3

22. Which of the following describes the effect of a catalyst?

	Activation energy	Enthalpy of reaction
A.	decreased	decreased
B.	decreased	increased
C.	unchanged	decreased
D.	decreased	unchanged

23. For the reaction $N_2(g)$ + $3H_2(g)$ $\rightleftharpoons$ $2NH_3(g)$

which statement about the catalyst is true?

A. It decreases the rate of the reverse reaction.
B. It decreases the heat released in the reaction.
C. It increases the activation energy.
D. It increases the rate of the reverse reaction.

24. Manganese dioxide speeds up the decomposition of hydrogen peroxide because it

A. increases the enthalpy change
B. increases the energy of activation
C. decreases the enthalpy change
D. decreases the energy of activation.

25. The reaction between oxalate ions and permanganate ions in the presence of hydrogen ions may be summarised:

When a little permanganate solution is added to hot (70 °C) acidic oxalate solution there is a time lag before the purple colour disappears; thereafter, with further additions of permanganate, the colour disappears instantly.

Which statement is a reasonable explanation of the instant disappearance of colour once the initial reaction has occured?

A. The reaction is endothermic.
B. The $Mn^{2+}(aq)$ which is formed catalyses the reaction.
C. The acid is a catalyst for the reaction.
D. The activation energy for the reaction is high.

26. The same reaction was carried out at four different temperatures. The table shows the times taken for the reaction to occur.

Temperature / ^{o}C	20	30	40	50
Time /s	60	30	14	5

The results show that

A. a small rise in temperature results in a large increase in reaction rate
B. the activation energy increases with increasing temperature
C. the rate of the reaction is directly proportional to the temperature
D. the reaction is endothermic.

27. A filter paper was dipped into a solution of phosphorus in carbon disulphide. After the carbon disulphide had evaporated, the filter paper caught fire. A filter paper dipped in pure carbon disulphide does not catch fire.

This indicates that

A. the burning of phosphorus has a negative activation energy
B. the evaporation of the carbon disulphide provides the activation energy for the burning of the phosphorus
C. the activation energy for the burning of the phosphorus is attainable at room temperature
D. phosphorus provides the activation energy for the evaporation of carbon disulphide.

28. Liquid petrol does not ignite spontaneously when exposed to the air because

A. the reaction is endothermic
B. the reaction between petrol and oxygen requires a catalyst
C. the reactants are in different physical states
D. not enough molecules possess sufficient energy to react.

29. Which of the following is **not** a factor which affects the rate of a reaction?

A. concentration of reactants
B. kinetic energies of reactants
C. activation energy of reaction
D. enthalpy change for the reaction

In questions 1 to 5 decide whether the enthalpy change in each of the processes is

A. endothermic　　**B.** exothermic.

1. $Cl_2(g) \rightarrow 2Cl(g)$

2. $Na(s) \rightarrow Na(g)$

3. $Na(g) \rightarrow Na^+(g) + e^-$

4. $Na^+(g) + Cl^-(g) \rightarrow Na^+Cl^-(s)$

5. $Cl(g) + e^- \rightarrow Cl^-(g)$

In questions 6 to 8 decide whether the enthalpy change in each of the reactions is

A. endothermic　　**B.** exothermic
C. either endothermic or exothermic

6. combustion

7. solution

8. neutralisation

9. Which equation represents an enthalpy of combustion?

A. $C_2H_6(g) + 3O_2(g) \rightarrow 2CO_2(g) + 3H_2O(l)$
B. $C_2H_5OH(l) + O_2(g) \rightarrow CH_3COOH(g) + H_2O(l)$
C. $CH_2CHO(l) + O_2(g) \rightarrow CH_2COOH(l)$
D. $CH_4(g) + 1^1/_2O_2(g) \rightarrow CO(g) + 2H_2O(l)$

10. Ethanol (C_2H_5OH) has a different enthalpy of combustion from dimethyl ether (CH_3OCH_3). This is mainly because the compounds have different

A. molecular masses
B. bonds within the molecules
C. products and combustion
D. boiling points.

11. A group of students added 6 g of ammonium chloride crystals to 200 cm^3 of water at a temperature of 25 $^{\circ}$C.

The enthalpy of solution of ammonium chloride is +13.6 kJ mol^{-1}.

After dissolving the crystals, the temperature of the solution would most likely be

A. 23 $^{\circ}$C   **B.** 25 $^{\circ}$C   **C.** 27 $^{\circ}$C   **D.** 30 $^{\circ}$C.

12. When 1 g of an alcohol (formula mass 46) is burned 30 kJ of energy is released.

What is the enthalpy of combustion, in kJ mol^{-1}, of the alcohol?

A. -30   **B.** -1380   **C.** -650   **D.** -1920.

13. What is the enthalpy change, in kJ, when 3.2 g of methanol is burned? (Use the enthalpy of combustion given in the data booklet.)

A. -72.7   **B.** +72.7   **C.** -727   **D.** +727

14. $H^+_{(aq)}$ + $OH^-_{(aq)}$ $\rightarrow$ $H_2O_{(l)}$ ΔH = - 57.5 kJ mol^{-1}

What is the amount of heat produced, in kJ, when 4.00 g of NaOH is just neutralised by HCl$_{(aq)}$?

A. 5.75   **B.** 28.7   **C.** 7.5   **D.** 15

15. What is the mass of ethanol, in grams, which has to be burned to produce 13.67 kJ?

(Use the enthalpy of combustion given in the data booklet.)

A. 0.46   **B.** 4.6   **C.** 13.67   **D.** 1367

16. When 1 g of a compound (formula mass 56) is dissolved in 50 cm^3 of water, the temperature rises by 4.7 $^{\circ}$C.

What is the enthalpy of solution, in kJ mol^{-1}, of the compound?

A. -55.0   **B.** -5.50   **C.** +5.50   **D.** +55.0

17. When 2.24 litres of a gas was burned, the heat produced warmed 2 litres of water from 12 $^{\circ}$C to 38 $^{\circ}$C.

What is the enthalpy of combustion, in kJ mol^{-1}, of the gas?
(Take the volume of one mole of gas to be 22.4 litres.)

A. -21.7   **B.** -217   **C.** -2170   **D.** -21 700

Questions 1 to 9 refer to trends associated with increasing atomic number in the alkali metals.

Decide whether each of the statements is

A. TRUE   **B.** FALSE.

1. The metallic bond strength increases.

2. The first ionisation energy decreases.

3. The atomic size decreases.

4. The number of occupied energy levels decreases.

5. The electronegativity decreases.

6. The melting point increases.

7. The tendency to form positive ions increases.

8. The nuclear charge increases.

9. The relative atomic mass decreases.

Questions 10 to 18 refer to trends associated with increasing atomic number in the halogens.

Decide whether each of the statements is

A. TRUE   **B.** FALSE.

10. The reactivity decreases.

11. The density decreases.

12. The first ionisation energy increases.

13. The boiling point increases.

14. The nuclear charge increases.

15. The electronegativity increases.

16. The relative atomic mass increases.

17. The atomic size increases.

18. The number of occupied energy levels increases.

Questions 19 to 23 refer to trends associated with increasing atomic number in the elements in the second period of the Periodic Table.

Decide whether each of the statements is

A. TRUE   **B.** FALSE.

19. The first ionisation energy increases.

20. The number of occupied energy levels increases.

21. The nuclear charge decreases.

22. The atomic size increases.

23. The electronegativity decreases.

Questions 24 and 25 refer to properties of elements.

A. caesium   **B.** oxygen
C. fluorine   **D.** iodine

24. Which element has the greatest electronegativity?

25. Which element has the lowest first ionisation energy?

26. Which property of the Group 1 elements could be represented by the graph?

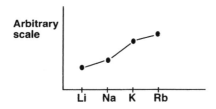

A. the first ionisation energy   **B.** the melting point
C. the atomic size   **D.** the electronegativity

27. Potassium has a larger atomic size than sodium because potassium has

A. a larger nuclear charge
B. a larger nucleus
C. more occupied energy levels
D. a larger first ionisation energy.

28. The difference between the atomic size of sodium and chlorine is mainly due to the difference in the

    A. number of electrons   **B.** number of protons

    C. number of neutrons   **D.** mass of each atom.

29. In which molecule will the chlorine atom carry a partial positive charge $(\delta+)$?

    A. Cl - Br   **B.** Cl - Cl   **C.** Cl - F   **D.** Cl - I

30. Which statement concerning the size of atoms and ions is correct?

The size of

    A. Cl^- is less than that of Cl

    B. H^- is greater than that of H^+

    C. Na^+ is greater than that of Na

    D. Fe^{3+} is greater than that of Fe^{2+}.

Questions 31 to 35 refer to the element francium (atomic number 87).

Decide whether each of the statements is likely to be

    A. TRUE   **B.** FALSE.

31. It will resist corrosion.

32. It will form a covalent chloride.

33. It will form a soluble hydroxide.

34. It will be very reactive.

35. It will conduct electricity.

Questions 36 to 40 refer to the element astatine (atomic number 85).

Decide whether each of the statements is likely to be

    A. TRUE   **B.** FALSE.

36. It will exist as diatomic molecules.

37. It will be a gas at room temperature.

38. It will form an ionic compound with sodium.

39. It will conduct electricity.

40. It will form a covalent hydride.

Questions 1 to 5 refer to what happens when an atom **X** of an element in Group 1 reacts to become an ion **X$^+$**.

Decide whether each of the statements is

A. TRUE   **B.** FALSE.

1. The atomic size increases.

2. The nucleus acquires a negative charge.

3. The number of energy levels (electron shells) decreases by one.

4. The atomic number decreases by one.

5. An electron is emitted from the nucleus.

6. Which equation represents the first ionisation energy of calcium?

A.	$Ca(s)$	$\rightarrow$	$Ca^+(g)$	$+$ e^-
B.	$Ca(s)$	$\rightarrow$	$Ca^+(aq)$	$+$ e^-
C.	$Ca(g)$	$\rightarrow$	$Ca^+(g)$	$+$ e^-
D.	$Ca(g)$	$\rightarrow$	$Ca^+(aq)$	$+$ e^-

7. Which equation represents the first ionisation energy of fluorine?

A.	$F(g) + e^- \rightarrow F^-(g)$
B.	$F(g) \rightarrow F^+(g) + e^-$
C.	$1/2F_2(g) \rightarrow F^-(g) + e^-$
D.	$F^+(g) + e^- \rightarrow F(g)$

8. Which element would require the most energy to convert one mole of gaseous atoms into gaseous ions carrying two positive charges?

   (You may wish to use the data booklet).

   A. scandium
   B. titanium
   C. vanadium
   D. chromium

9. The spike graph shows the variation in the first ionisation energy with atomic number for sixteen consecutive elements in the Periodic Table. The element at which the spike graph starts is not specified.

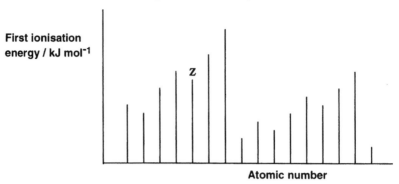

In which group of the Periodic Table is element **Z**?

A. 1

B. 3

C. 5

D. 6

Questions 10 and 11 refer to the ionisation energies of four elements

	1st Ionisation energy/kJ mol^{-1}	2nd Ionisation energy/kJ mol^{-1}	3rd Ionisation energy/kJ mol^{-1}
A.	1690	3380	6060
B.	502	4560	6920
C.	556	1080	4120
D.	584	1830	2760

10. Which element is most likely to form an ion of the type X^+?

11. Which element is most likely to form an ion of the type X^{2+}?

Test 1.11   The first twenty elements

The questions in this test refer to types of bonding and structure.

    A.   metallic
    B.   covalent (network)
    C.   covalent (molecular gas)
    D.   covalent (molecular solid)
    E.   monatomic

What is the type of bonding and structure which predominates at room temperature in each of the elements?

1.	aluminium	12.	hydrogen
2.	argon	13.	lithium
3.	beryllium	14.	neon
4.	nitrogen	15.	boron
5.	calcium	16.	oxygen
6.	carbon (diamond)	17.	carbon (graphite)
7.	sulphur	18.	potassium
8.	fluorine	19.	silicon
9.	magnesium	20.	sodium
10.	helium	21.	chlorine
11.	carbon (fullerenes)	22.	phosphorus

Test 1.12   Types of bonding and structure (i)

In questions 1 to 3 decide whether each of the following statements refers to

A.   diamond   **B.**   graphite.

1. has delocalised electrons

2. has layers held together by van der Waals' forces

3. has a three-dimensional structure based on tetrahedrons

Questions 4 to 11 refer to types of structure.

A.   covalent (molecular)   **B.**   covalent (network)
C.   ionic

What type of structure predominates in each of the compounds?

4. hydrogen bromide

5. sodium nitrate

6. silicon carbide

7. carbon tetrachloride

8. magnesium oxide

9. silicon dioxide

10. sulphur dioxide

11. potassium sulphate

Questions 12 to 14 refer to the formation of chlorides.

A.   lithium   **B.**   caesium
C.   sulphur   **D.**   phosphorus
E.   xenon

12. Which element forms the chloride which is most ionic in character?

13. Which element forms the chloride which is most covalent in character?

14. Which element is least likely to form a chloride?

15. In the diagram, each sphere represents a particle about the size of an atom and the sign indicates the charge on the particle.

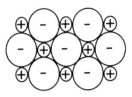

For which substance would the model be a reasonable representation of the particles and the way they are arranged in the crystal?

A. tetrabromomethane
B. calcium flouride
C. lithium bromide
D. diamond

Questions 17 and 18 refer to the diagrams which represent molecules.

| represents an electron pair in the plane of the paper;

△ represents an electron pair in front of the plane of the paper;

⠘⠄ represents an electron pair behind the plane of the paper.

16. Which elements could make up structure (i) ?

	R	T
A.	nitrogen	hydrogen
B.	hydrogen	nitrogen
C.	carbon	hydrogen
D.	beryllium	chlorine

17. Which elements could make up structure (ii) ?

	Z	Q
A.	oxygen	hydrogen
B.	hydrogen	oxygen
C.	beryllium	hydrogen
D.	phosphorus	hydrogen

18. Which pair of elements would be expected to react together with the greatest release of energy?

    A. potassium and bromine
    B. caesium and fluorine
    C. lithium and iodine
    D. sodium and chlorine

19. Which statement may be correctly applied to silicon dioxide?

    A. It consists of discrete molecules.
    B. It has a covalent network structure.
    C. It is similar in structure to carbon dioxide.
    D. Van der Waals' attractions are important to its structure.

Test 1.13   Types of bonding and structure (ii)

Questions 1 to 5 refer to types of attraction.

Decide whether each of the following is

A.   intermolecular   **B.**   **NOT** intermolecular.

1. covalent bonds

2. ionic bonds

3. hydrogen bonds

4. metallic bonds

5. van der Waals' forces

Questions 6 to 17 refer to intermolecular attractions.

A.   van der Waals' forces   **B.**   hydrogen bonds
C.   permanent dipole-permanent dipole interactions but **no** hydrogen bonds

What is the main intermolecular attraction in each of the liquids?

6. neon

7. butane

8. methanol, CH_3-OH

9. hydrogen

10. hydrogen bromide

11. propanoic acid, CH_3-CH_2-$\overset{\overset{\displaystyle O}{\|}}{C}$-OH

12. hydrogen oxide

13. nitrogen hydride

14. ethyl ethanoate, CH_3-$\overset{\overset{\displaystyle O}{\|}}{C}$-O-$CH_2$-$CH_3$

15. hydrogen fluoride

16. octene

17. propanone, CH_3-$\overset{\overset{\displaystyle O}{\|}}{C}$-$CH_3$

Question 18 to 24 refer to types of attraction.

A. non-polar covalent bonds   **B.** polar covalent bonds
C. hydrogen bonds   **D.** van der Waals' forces

What type of attraction is mainly responsible for holding each of the pairs together?

18. two adjacent ethanol molecules

19. the carbon atom and a chlorine atom in a molecule of tetrachloromethene

20. two chlorine atoms in a molecule of chlorine

21. a hydrogen atom and the oxygen atom in a molecule of water

22. two adjacent hexene molecules in hexene

23. the carbon atom and an oxygen atom in a molecule of carbon dioxide

24. two adjacent molecules of hydrogen fluoride

Questions 25 to 28 refer to types of structure.

A. three dimensional ionic lattice
B. three dimensional covalently linked structure
C. three dimensional structure of molecules, linked by hydrogen bonds
D. linear covalent structure, linked by van der Waals' forces

Which type best describes the structure of each of the following?

25. ice

26. silicon dioxide

27. potassium chloride

28. polystyrene

Questions 29 to 38 refer to types of attraction.

A.	ionic bonds	**B.**	hydrogen bonds
C.	van der Waals' forces	**D.**	covalent bonds
E.	permanent dipole-permanent dipole interactions		

What is the main type of attraction which is overcome in melting each of the following?

29. caesium fluoride

30. hydrogen fluoride

31. fluorine

32. silicon

33. hydrogen oxide

34. hydrogen sulphide

35. methane

36. boron

37. sulphur dioxide

38. rubidium chloride

39. Which of the following shows the types of bonding forces in decreasing order of strength?

    A.   covalent : hydrogen : van der Waals'
    B.   covalent : van der Waals' : hydrogen
    C.   hydrogen : covalent : van der Waals
    D.   van der Waals' : hydrogen : covalent

40. Which of the following occurs when crude oil is distilled?

    A.   Covalent bonds break and form again.
    B.   Covalent bonds break and van der Waals' bonds form.
    C.   Van der Waals' bonds break and covalent bonds form.
    D.   Van der Waals' bonds break and form again.

Test 1.14

Properties of elements and compounds

In questions 1 to 11 decide whether each of the substances

A. conducts electricity   **B.** does **NOT** conduct electricity.

1. liquid oxygen

2. solid phosphorus pentachloride

3. molten potassium chloride

4. liquid tetrachloromethane

5. solid carbon (graphite)

6. solid sodium chloride

7. molten copper

8. solid sulphur

9. solid carbon (diamond)

10. calcium chloride solution

11. solid iron

In questions 12 to 14 decide whether each of the following statements refers to

A. diamond   **B.** graphite.

12. is used as a cutting tip

13. is used as a lubricant

14. is used as 'lead' in pencils

Question 15 and 16 refer to types of bonding.

A. metallic   **B.** polar covalent
C. non-polar covalent   **D.** ionic

Which type of bonding is likely to be present in each of the following?

15. an element which melts at 3500 $^{\circ}$C and forms a gaseous oxide

16. a compound of nitrogen which boils at -33 $^{\circ}$C

Questions 17 to 22 refer to types of bonding.

A.	covalent (discrete molecules)	**B.**	ionic
C.	covalent (network structure)	**D.**	metallic

Which type of bonding predominates in each of the following?

17. a substance which melts at 1044 °C and which conducts electricity when molten, but not when solid

18. a substance which melts at 962 °C and conducts electricity when solid

19. a substance which melts at 843 °C and boils at 1540 °C; when an electric current is passed through the molten substance no decomposition occurs

20. a substance of melting point 2300 °C, boiling point of 2550 °C, which does not conduct electricity

21. a substance melting at 1074 °C and boiling at 1740 °C; the passage of an electric current through the molten substance results in decomposition

22. a substance which melts at 6 °C and boils at 80 °C, which does not conduct electricity

Questions 23 to 26 refer to properties of elements and compounds.

A.	potassium fluoride	**B.**	silicon oxide
C.	sulphur	**D.**	sodium

23. Which is a solid of low melting point with high electrical conductivity?

24. Which is a non-conducting solid which becomes a good conductor on melting?

25. Which is a solid of high melting point with no electrical conductivity?

26. Which is a solid of low melting point with no electrical conductivity?

27. In general, covalent substances have lower melting points than ionic substances because

   A. ionic bonds are stronger than covalent bonds
   B. covalent compounds are composed of non-metals which have low melting points
   C. bonds between molecules are weaker than bonds between ions
   D. covalent bonds have no electrostatic forces.

28. Which substance is insoluble in water but soluble in tetrachloromethane?

A.	iodine	**B.**	sodium chloride
C.	potassium iodide	**D.**	lithium bromide

29. An ionic compound is likely to

    A.   have a low melting point

    B.   dissolve in non-polar solvents

    C.   be an electrical insulator when molten

    D.   be soluble in water.

30. Silicon carbide can be used as

    A.   a lubricant

    B.   a tip for cutting / grinding tools

    C.   a substitute for pencil 'lead'

    D.   an electrical conductor.

31. Information about four solids, **A, B, C** and **D,** is shown.

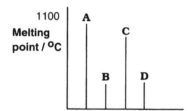

Electrical conduction of solid	
A.	non-conductor
B.	conductor
C.	conductor
D.	non-conductor

In which solid is it most likely that only van der Waals' forces are overcome when the substance melts?

32.

Substance **X**,
molecular mass 62

Substance **Y**,
molecular mass 64.5

From a consideration of chemical bonding, what can you predict about the boiling points of these compounds?

    A.   The boiling point of **X** is greater than that of **Y**.

    B.   The boiling point of **X** is less than that of **Y**.

    C.   The boiling point of **X** is approximately equal to that of **Y**.

    D.   Nothing can be predicted.

33. In general, covalent substances have lower melting points than ionic substances because

A. ionic bonds are stronger than covalent bonds
B. covalent compounds are composed of non-metals which have low melting points
C. bonds between molecules are weaker than bonds between ions
D. covalent bonds have no electrostatic forces.

34. Which chloride is most likely to be soluble in tetrachloromethane?

A. barium chloride
B. caesium chloride
C. calcium chloride
D. phosphorus chloride

35. Which oxide would be a solid at room temperature and a gas at $400^\circ C$.
(You may wish to use the data booklet.)

A. fluorine oxide
B. phosphorus oxide
C. magnesium oxide
D. boron oxide

36. Carbon dioxide is a gas at room temperature while silicon dioxide is a solid because

A. van der Waals' forces are much weaker than covalent bonds
B. carbon dioxide contains double covalent bonds and silicon dioxide contains single covalent bonds
C. carbon-oxygen bonds are less polar than silicon-oxygen bonds
D. the relative formula mass of carbon dioxide is less than that of silicon dioxide.

37. Molten lithium hydride can be electrolysed using platinum electrodes.

What is the reaction taking place at the positive electrode?

A. $2H^-(l) \rightarrow H_2(g) + 2e^-$

B. $2H^+(l) + 2e^- \rightarrow H_2(g)$

C. $Li^+(l) + e^- \rightarrow Li(l)$

D. $Li(l) \rightarrow Li^+(l) + e^-$

38. The diagram shows the melting points of successive elements across a period in the Periodic Table.

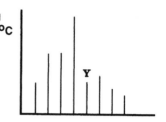

Melting point / °C

Which is a correct reason for the low melting point of element **Y**?

A. It has weak ionic bonds.

B. It has weak covalent bonds.

C. It has weakly held outer electrons.

D. It has weak forces between molecules.

Test 1.15 Polarity of molecules

(For each of the questions in this test, **three** answers should be given.)

Decide whether each of the molecules

A. has polar bonds
B. has non-polar bonds
C. is overall polar
D. is overall non-polar
E. is three-dimensional
F. is planar
G. is linear

1. H_2
2. CCl_4
3. HCl
4. H_2O
5. CO_2
6. NH_3
7. $CHCl_3$
8. CH_3OH

1. What is the mass, in grams, of 0.25 mol of carbon dioxide?

   A. 7 **B.** 11 **C.** 15 **D.** 19

2. How many moles are contained in 5 g sodium hydroxide?

   A. 0.1 **B.** 0.125 **C.** 0.25 **D.** 0.5

3. How many moles of sodium hydroxide must be dissolved to make 200 cm^3 of 2 mol l^{-1} solution?

   A. 0.02 **B.** 0.04 **C.** 0.2 **D.** 0.4

4. What is the concentration, in mol l^{-1}, of a solution which contains 0.5 mol of hydrogen chloride dissolved in 200 cm^3 of solution?

   A. 0.2 **B.** 0.5 **C.** 1.0 **D.** 2.5

5. What volume of a 0.2 mol l^{-1} solution contains 1 mol?

   A. 200 cm^3 **B.** 500 cm^3 **C.** 1 litre **D.** 5 litres

6. What mass of sodium carbonate, in grams, is required to make 50 cm^3 of 0.1 mol l^{-1} solution?

   A. 0.53 **B.** 1.06 **C.** 5.3 **D.** 10.6

7. What is the concentration of a solution, in mol l^{-1}, containing 4 g of sodium hydroxide in 100 cm^3 of water?

   A. 0.01 **B.** 0.4 **C.** 1 **D.** 4

8. 0.5 mol of copper(II) chloride and 0.5 mol of copper(II) sulphate are dissolved in water and made up to 500 cm^3 of solution.

   What is the concentration, in mol l^{-1}, of Cu^{2+} (aq) ions in the solution ?

   A. 0.5 **B.** 1.0 **C.** 2.0 **D.** 4.0

9. A mixture of magnesium chloride and magnesium sulphate is known to contain 0.6 mol of chloride ion and 0.2 mol of sulphate ion.

   How many moles of magnesium ions are present?

   A. 0.4   **B.** 0.5   **C.** 0.8   **D.** 1.0

10. A mixture of sodium chloride and sodium sulphate is known to contain 0.5 mol of sodium ions and 0.2 mol of chloride ions.

    How many moles of sulphate ions are present?

    A. 0.15   **B.** 0.20   **C.** 0.25   **D.** 0.30

11. A mixture of sodium chloride and sodium sulphate is known to contain 0.6 mol of chloride ion and 0.2 mol of sulphate ion.

    How many moles of sodium ions are present?

    A. 0.4   **B.** 0.5   **C.** 0.8   **D.** 1.0

12. A mixture of magnesium bromide and magnesium sulphate is known to contain 3 mol of magnesium and 4 mol of bromide ions.

    How many moles of sulphate ions are present?

    A. 1   **B.** 2   **C.** 3   **D.** 4

13. A mixture of sodium sulphate and copper(II) sulphate is known to contain 3 mol of sulphate ions and 1 mol of copper ions.

    How many moles of sodium ions are present?

    A. 1   **B.** 2   **C.** 3   **D.** 4

Test 1.17

The mole (ii)

1. Which solid contains the greatest number of atoms?

   A. 20 g of carbon   **B.** 20 g of calcium
   C. 20 g of magnesium   **D.** 20 g of sulphur

2. Which gas contains the smallest number of molecules?

   A. 100 g of fluorine   **B.** 100 g of nitrogen
   C. 100 g of oxygen   **D.** 100 g of hydrogen

3. Which gas contains the greatest number of molecules?

   A. 0.10 g of hydrogen gas   **B.** 0.17 g of ammonia gas
   C. 0.32 g of methane gas   **D.** 0.16 g of oxygen gas

4. Which gas contains the greatest number of atoms?

   A. 1 g of hydrogen   **B.** 32 g of oxygen
   C. 20 g of neon   **D.** 40 g of argon

5. 160 g of calcium contains as many atoms as

   A. 28 g of carbon   **B.** 92 g of sodium
   C. 54 g of aluminium   **D.** 310 g of phosphorus.

6. 97.2 g of magnesium contains twice as many atoms as

   A. 51 g of vanadium   **B.** 2 mol of oxygen molecules
   C. 2 mol of calcium   **D.** 48 g of carbon.

7. Which of the following contains the greatest number of atoms?

   A. 12 g of carbon   **B.** 9 g of hydrogen oxide
   C. 16 g of oxygen   **D.** 14 g of carbon monoxide

8. Which of the following contains the smallest number of hydrogen atoms?

   A. 17 g of ammonia (NH_3)   **B.** 16 g of methane (CH_4)
   C. 36 g of water (H_2O)   **D.** 14 g of ethene (C_2H_4)

9. 4 g of sodium hydroxide contains the same number of ions as

   A. 17 g of sodium nitrate   **B.** 10 g of calcium carbonate
   C. 16.4 g of calcium nitrate   **D.** 10.6 g of sodium carbonate.

10. What is the amount, in moles, of oxygen atoms in 0.5 mol of carbon dioxide?

    A. 0.25   **B.** 0.5   **C.** 1   **D.** 2

11. One mole of calcium chloride contains

    A. 3 mol of atoms   **C.** 1 mol of positive ions
    B. 1 mol of molecules   **D.** 1 mol of negative ions.

12. 36 g of hydrogen oxide contains

    A. 2 mol of hydrogen atoms
    B. 1 mol of atoms
    C. 4 mol of hydrogen atoms
    D. 2 mol of atoms.

13. Which of the following is **not** found in 1 g of hydrogen gas?

    A. 1 mol of electrons   **C.** 1 mol of atoms
    B. 1 mol of protons   **D.** 1 mol of molecules.

14. In which of the following pairs do the gases contain the same number of atoms of oxygen?

    A. 1 mol of oxygen and 1 mol of carbon monoxide
    B. 1 mol of oxygen and 0.5 mol of carbon dioxide
    C. 0.5 mol of oxygen and 1 mol of carbon dioxide
    D. 1 mol of oxygen and 1 mol of carbon dioxide

15. Which of the following contains one mole of neutrons?

    A. 1 g of $_{1}^{1}H$
    B. 1 g of $_{6}^{12}C$
    C. 2 g of $_{12}^{24}Mg$
    D. 2 g of $_{10}^{22}Ne$

Test 1.18   The Avogadro Constant (i)

For the questions in this test decide whether each of the statements is

A.   TRUE   **B.**   FALSE.

The Avogadro Constant is the same as the number of

1. atoms in 24 g of carbon

2. atoms in 0.5 mol of chlorine molecules

3. molecules in 0.5 mol of carbon monoxide

4. atoms in 16 g of oxygen

5. molecules in 2 g of hydrogen

6. ions in 1 litre of sodium chloride solution, concentration 1 mol l^{-1}

7. ions in 0.5 mol of sodium oxide

8. electrons in 0.5 mol of helium atoms

9. protons in 2 g of sulphur.

Questions 10 to 13 refer to 17 g of ammonia, 2 g of hydrogen and 71 g of chlorine.

10. Each occupies the same volume.

11. Each contains 6×10^{23} atoms.

12. Each contains 6×10^{23} molecules.

Questions 13 to 18 refer to carbon dioxide gas.

13. The mass of 6×10^{23} molecules is 44 g.

14. One molecule is 44 times as heavy as a molecule of hydrogen.

15. 44 g occupy the same volume as 32 g oxygen.

16. 44 g of the gas contains the same number of atoms as 20 g of neon.

17. 44 g of the gas contains 6×10^{23} carbon atoms

18. 44 g of the gas contains the same number of molecules as 1 g of hydrogen.

Questions 19 to 24 refer to the Avogadro Constant.

19. 64 g of sulphur contains 6×10^{23} atoms.

20. 1 g of hydrogen contains 6×10^{23} molecules.

21. 500 cm^3 of 2 mol l^{-1} sodium hydroxide solution contains 6×10^{23} sodium ions.

22. 6 g of water contains 6×10^{23} atoms.

23. 64 g of sulphur dioxide contains 6×10^{23} atoms.

24. 1 litre of 1 mol l^{-1} sulphuric acid contains 6×10^{23} sulphate ions.

1. How many atoms are in 20 g of calcium?

    A. 1×10^{23} **B.** 3×10^{23} **C.** 6×10^{23} **D.** 1.2×10^{24}

2. How many molecules are in 3.2 g of methane?

    A. 1×10^{23} **B.** 1.2×10^{23} **C.** 6×10^{23} **D.** 3×10^{24}

3. How many atoms are in 0.5 mol of fluorine?

    A. 1.5×10^{23} **B.** 3×10^{23} **C.** 6×10^{23} **D.** 1.2×10^{24}

4. How many atoms are in 0.44 g of carbon dioxide?

    A. 1.8×10^{22} **B.** 6×10^{22} **C.** 1.2×10^{23} **D.** 1.8×10^{23}

5. How many ions are in 20 g of sodium hydroxide?

    A. 3×10^{22} **B.** 6×10^{22} **C.** 3×10^{23} **D.** 6×10^{23}

6. How many ions in 11.1 g of calcium chloride?

    A. 6×10^{22} **B.** 1.2×10^{23} **C.** 1.8×10^{23} **D.** 2.4×10^{23}

7. The molecular formula for a gas is X_3.
    How many **X** atoms will be present in 0.25 mol of **X**?

    A. $0.5 \times 6 \times 10^{23}$ **B.** $0.75 \times 6 \times 10^{23}$
    C. $1 \times 6 \times 10^{23}$ **D.** $3 \times 6 \times 10^{23}$

8. How many protons are in 120 g of carbon?

    A. 60   **B.** 1×10^{24} **C.** 6×10^{24} **D.** 3.6×10^{25}

9. How many electrons are in 1.215 g of magnesium ions?

    A. 3×10^{22} **B.** 3.6×10^{22} **C.** 3.6×10^{23} **D.** 6×10^{24}

10. Deuterium (^{2}H) is a heavy isotope of hydrogen.
    How many neutrons are in 10 g of deuterium atoms?

    A. 3×10^{23} **B.** 6×10^{23} **C.** 3×10^{24} **D.** 6×10^{24}

11. What is the mass, in grams, of one sodium atom?

    A. 6×10^{23} **B.** 6×10^{-23}

    C. 3.8×10^{-23} **D.** 3.8×10^{-24}

12. What is the mass, in grams, of 100 molecules of hydrogen?

    A. 6×10^{23} **B.** 1.66×10^{-22}

    C. 3.33×10^{-22} **D.** 1.2×10^{-23}

13. Fullerene molecules consist of 60 carbon atoms.

Approximately how many such molecules are present in 12 g of this type of carbon?

    A. 1.0×10^{22} **B.** 1.2×10^{23} **C.** 6.0×10^{23} **D.** 3.6×10^{25}

14. Diabetics suffer from a deficiency of the protein insulin (relative formula mass 6000).

What mass of insulin will contain approximately 3×10^{20} molecules?

    A. 3 g   **B.** 6 g   **C.** 30 g   **D.** 60 g

15. A one carat diamond used in a ring contained approximately 1×10^{22} carbon atoms.

What is the mass of the diamond?

    A. 0.1 g   **B.** 0.2 g   **C.** 1.0 g   **D.** 1.2 g

Test 1.20   **Molar volume**

For the questions in this test assume that all measurements are made at the same temperature and pressure.

1. Which gas has the smallest volume?

   A. 10 g of oxygen   **B.** 10 g of carbon monoxide
   C. 10 g of ethane (C_2H_6)   **D.** 10 g of hydrogen

2. Which gas has the greatest volume?

   A. 1 g of hydrogen   **B.** 14 g of nitrogen
   C. 20 g of neon   **D.** 35.5 g of chlorine

3. Which gas has the same volume as 1 g of helium?

   A. 1.6 g of methane   **B.** 2.2 g of carbon dioxide
   C. 3.6 g of hydrogen oxide **D.** 16 g of sulphur dioxide

4. Given equal volumes of each gas, in which pair do both gases have the same mass?

   A. hydrogen and helium   **B.** methane and oxygen
   C. ethene and nitrogen   **D.** carbon monoxide and
                                            nitrogen monoxide

5. Which gas has the highest density?

   A. CO   **B.** NO   **C.** N_2 **D.** C_2H_4

6. The volume of 1 g of hydrogen is 11.4 litres.

   What is the volume, in litres, of 2 mol of hydrogen?

   A. 5.7   **B.** 11.4
   C. 22.8   **D.** 45.6

7. A gaseous hydrocarbon has a density of 1.25 g l^{-1}. The molar volume of the gas is 22.2 litres.

   What is the molecular formula?

   A. CH_4 **B.** C_2H_4
   C. C_3H_6 **D.** C_4H_8

8. The density of chlorine gas is found to be 3.00 gl^{-1}.

   Under these conditions, the molar volume, in litres is

   A. 11.8   **B.** 22.4   **C.** 23.7   **D.** 35.5

9. Using the density quoted in the data booklet, what is the number of moles of nitrogen molecules in a 5 litre container?

   A. 0.11   **B.** 0.23   **C.** 0.35   **D.** 0.47

   In questions 10 to 12 take the molar volume to be 23 litres mol^{-1}.

10. What is the volume, in litres, of 2 g of neon?

    A. 1   **B.** 2   **C.** 2.3   **D.** 23

11. How many molecules are in 2.3 litres of oxygen?

    A. 6×10^{22} **B.** 1.2×10^{23} **C.** 6×10^{23} **D.** 1.2×10^{24}

12. How many atoms are in 0.23 litres of hydrogen?

    A. 6×10^{21} **B.** 1.2×10^{22} **C.** 6×10^{22} **D.** 1.2×10^{23}

Test 1.21   Calculations based on equations (i)

1. $2CO_{(g)} + O_{2(g)} \rightarrow 2CO_{2(g)}$

    What mass, in grams, of carbon dioxide would be obtained by the combustion of 28 g carbon monoxide?

    A. 28   **B.** 44   **C.** 56   **D.** 88

2. $CH_{4(g)} + 2O_{2(g)} \rightarrow CO_{2(g)} + 2H_2O_{(l)}$

    What mass, in grams, of methane is required to produce 1.8 g of water?

    A. 0.8   **B.** 1.6   **C.** 8.0   **D.** 16.0

Questions 3 to 8 refer to the neutralisation of 20 cm^3 of sodium hydroxide solution, concentration 0.2 mol l^{-1}, by acids.

Decide whether each of the acids

A.   can neutralise the alkali to form a neutral solution
B.   can **NOT** neutralise the alkali to form a neutral solution.

3. 20 cm^3 hydrochloric acid, concentration 0.2 mol l^{-1}

4. 40 cm^3 hydrochloric acid, concentration 0.1 mol l^{-1}

5. 10 cm^3 hydrochloric acid, concentration 0.2 mol l^{-1}

6. 20 cm^3 sulphuric acid, concentration 0.2 mol l^{-1}

7. 20 cm^3 sulphuric acid , concentration 0.1 mol l^{-1}

8. 10 cm^3 sulphuric acid, concentration 0.2 mol l^{-1}

9. 50 cm^3 of sulphuric acid, concentration, 2 mol l^{-1}, required 100 cm^3 of sodium hydroxide solution for complete neutralisation.

    What was the concentration, in mol l^{-1}, of the sodium hydroxide solution ?

    A. 0.25   **B.** 0.5   **C.** 1   **D.** 2

10. When 2 g hydrogen is exploded in excess oxygen, how many moles of steam are produced?

    A. 0.5   **B.** 1   **C.** 2   **D.** 3

11. Calcium carbonate can be decomposed by heating.

How many moles of carbon dioxide would be produced by the complete decomposition of 1 mol of calcium carbonate?

- **A.** 1.0
- **B.** 0.5
- **C.** 2.0
- **D.** It is impossible to say without knowing the temperature and pressure.

12. 1 mol of an alkane required 8 mol of oxygen for complete combustion.

Which of the following is the formula for the alkane?

A. C_3H_8 **B.** C_4H_{10} **C.** C_5H_{12} **D.** C_6H_{14}

13. Which alkanol will give 7 mol of carbon dioxide when 1 mol of it is completely burned?

- **A.** $CH_3CH_2CH(OH)CH(CH_3)_2$
- **B.** $(CH_3)_3CCH_2OH$
- **C.** $CH_3CH_2CH_2CH(OH)CH_2CH_2CH_3$
- **D.** $(CH_3)_2CHCH(OH)\ C(CH_3)_3$

14. If 1 mol of equally fine granules of three metals reacted with equal volumes of excess hydrochloric acid, which one should give off the most hydrogen?

- **A.** aluminium   **B.** magnesium
- **C.** lithium   **D.** They should all give same

15. $NO_3^-(aq)$ + $4H^+(aq)$ + $3e^-$ $\rightarrow$ $NO(g)$ + $2H_2O(l)$

$Cu(s)$ $\rightarrow$ $Cu^{2+}(aq)$ + $2e^-$

The equations represent a reaction between nitric acid and copper.
How many moles of $NO_3^-(aq)$ are required to oxidise 63.5 g of copper?

A. $2/3$ **B.** 1   **C.** $3/2$ **D.** 2

16. A pupil obtained a certain volume of carbon dioxide by the action of 20 cm^3 of hydrochloric acid, concentration 2 mol l^{-1}, on excess of sodium carbonate.

Which reagent gives the same final volume of carbon dioxide when added to excess sodium carbonate?

   A.   20 cm^3 of hydrochloric acid, concentration 4 mol l^{-1}

   B.   10 cm^3 of hydrochloric acid, concentration 4 mol l^{-1}

   C.   20 cm^3 of sulphuric acid, concentration 2 mol l^{-1}

   D.   40 cm^3 of hydrochloric acid, concentration 2 mol l^{-1}

In questions 17 to 21 take the molar volume of the gases to be 23.0 litres mol^{-1}.

17. How many litres of oxygen are needed to react completely with 1 mol of calcium?

   A. 5.75   **B.** 11.5   **C.** 23.0   **D.** 46.0

18. In the reaction $2C(s) + O_2(g) \rightarrow 2CO(g)$
what mass of carbon, in grams, will be used to form 23.0 litres of CO?

   A. 0.6   **B.** 1.2   **C.** 6.0   **D.** 12.0

19. What volume of chlorine, in litres, will be produced when 1 mol of hydrochloric acid reacts according to the equation:

   $MnO_2(s) + 4HCl(aq) \rightarrow MnCl_2(aq) + 2H_2O(l) + Cl_2(g)$

   A. 5.75   **B.** 11.5   **C.** 23.0   **D.** 92.0

20. How many litres of hydrogen are needed to reduce 1 mol of iron(III) oxide completely to the metal?

   A. 11.5   **B.** 23.0   **C.** 46.0   **D.** 69.0

21. Potassium chlorate ($KClO_3$) can decompose on heating to give potassium chloride and oxygen.

What volume of oxygen, in litres, would be produced by the complete decomposition of 1 mol of potassium chlorate?

   A. 11.5   **B.** 23.0   **C.** 34.5   **D.** 46

Test 1.22   Calculations based on equations (ii)

For the questions in this test assume that all measurements are made at the same temperature and pressure.

Questions 1 to 6 refer to reactions involving gases.

Decide whether the total volume of products will be

A.   less than the total volume of reactants

B.   equal to the total volume of reactants

C.   greater than the total volume of reactants.

1. $2NH_3(g) \rightarrow N_2(g) + 3H_2(g)$

2. $H_2(g) + Cl_2(g) \rightarrow 2HCl(g)$

3. $N_2(g) + 2O_2(g) \rightarrow 2NO_2(g)$

4. $C(s) + O_2(g) \rightarrow CO_2(g)$

5. $C_2H_4(g) + 3O_2(g) \rightarrow 2CO_2(g) + 2H_2O(l)$

6. $Fe_2O_3(s) + 3CO(g) \rightarrow 2Fe(s) + 3CO_2(g)$

7. The reaction of hydrogen and oxygen is represented by the equation:

   $H_2(g) + {}^1/_2O_2(g) \rightarrow H_2O(g)$

   What is the volume of oxygen, in litres, which reacts with 1 litre of hydrogen?

   A. $^1/_4$ **B.** $^1/_2$ **C.** 1   **D.** 2

8. What volume of oxygen, in litres, is required for the complete combustion of 1 litre of butane?

   A. 1   **B.** 4   **C.** 6.5   **D.** 13

9. How many litres of carbon dioxide would be obtained by the complete combustion of 2 litres of ethene?

   A. 2   **B.** 4   **C.** 6   **D.** 8

10. What volume of oxygen, in litres, would be required for the complete combustion of a gaseous mixture containing 1 litre of carbon monoxide and 3 litres of hydrogen?

A. 1   **B.** 2   **C.** 3   **D.** 4

11. $N_{2(g)} + 2O_{2(g)} \rightarrow 2NO_{2(g)}$

How many litres of nitrogen dioxide gas could be obtained by sparking 5 litres of nitrogen gas with 2 litres of oxygen gas?

A. 2   **B.** 3   **C.** 4   **D.** 5

12. $2NO_{(g)} + O_{2(g)} \rightarrow 2NO_{2(g)}$

How many litres of nitrogen dioxide gas could be obtained by mixing 3 litres of nitrogen monoxide gas and 1 litre of oxygen gas?

A. 2   **B.** 3   **C.** 4   **D.** 5

13. A mixture of 11.2 litres of oxygen and 11.2 litres of hydrogen is sparked.

What is the total number of molecules which react?

(Take the molar volume of the gases to be 22.4 litres mol^{-1}.)

A. 3×10^{23} **B.** 4.5×10^{23}
C. 6×10^{23} **D.** 9×10^{23}

14. The composition of air by volume is approximately 20% oxygen, 80% nitrogen.

When air is passed through red-hot carbon, the following reaction occurs:

$2C_{(s)} + O_{2(g)} \rightarrow 2CO_{(g)}$

If all the oxygen is converted to carbon monoxide, what is the composition, by volume, of the gas produced?

A. 20% carbon monoxide, 80% nitrogen
B. 33% carbon monoxide, 66% nitrogen
C. 40% carbon monoxide, 60% nitrogen
D. 50% carbon monoxide, 50% nitrogen

15. What volume of carbon dioxide, in cm^3, would be obtained by the combustion of 28 cm^3 of carbon monoxide?

   A.   28   **B.**   42   **C.**   56   **D.**   84

16. A volume of 10 cm^3 of carbon monoxide was passed over heated copper(II) oxide until no further reaction occured.

   What volume of gas, in cm^3, was obtained?

   A.   0   **B.**   10   **C.**   15   **D.**   20

17. $3CuO_{(s)}$ + $2NH_{3(g)}$ $\rightarrow$ $3Cu_{(s)}$ + $N_{2(g)}$ + $3H_2O_{(l)}$

   What volume of gas, in cm^3, would be obtained by the reaction between 100 cm^3 of ammonia gas and excess copper(II) oxide?

   A.   50   **B.**   100   **C.**   200   **D.**   400

18. The equation for the complete combustion of propane is:

   $C_3H_{8(g)}$ + $5O_{2(g)}$ $\rightarrow$ $3CO_{2(g)}$ + $4H_2O_{(l)}$

   50 cm^3 of propane is mixed with 500 cm^3 of oxygen and the mixture is ignited.

   What is the volume, in cm^3, of the resulting gas mixture?

   A.   150   **B.**   300   **C.**   400   **D.**   700

   Questions 19 and 20 refer to the following experiment.

   A mixture of 50 cm^3 of carbon monoxide and 40 cm^3 carbon dioxide is heated with excess copper(II) oxide until no further reaction occurs.

19. What is the total volume of gas, in cm^3, after the reaction?

   A.   40   **B.**   50   **C.**   90   **D.**   140

20. If the gases are **first** passed through an aqueous solution of sodium hydroxide, what is the volume, in cm^3, of the remaining gas?

   A.   40   **B.**   50   **C.**   90   **D.**   140

Questions 21 and 22 refer to the combustion of methane.

15 cm^3 of methane was collected in a tube over mercury and 35 cm^3 of oxygen was added. The mixture was then sparked to burn the methane. The reaction is:

$$CH_4(g) \quad + \quad 2O_2(g) \quad \rightarrow \quad CO_2(g) \quad + \quad 2H_2O(l)$$

21. What was the volume, in cm^3, of the gas remaining after the explosion?

    A. 20   **B.** 45   **C.** 50   **D.** 55

22. If a small volume of sodium hydroxide solution was injected into the tube after the explosion, what would be the volume, in cm^3, of the remaining gas?

    A. 5   **B.** 15   **C.** 30   **D.** 45

1. Which hydrocarbon is most likely to be found in petrol?

   A. C_2H_6 **B.** C_7H_{16}

   C. $C_{15}H_{32}$ **D.** $C_{20}H_{42}$

2. During the manufacture of petrol, the process of reforming is used to produce a petrol with a higher percentage of molecules which are

   A. unsaturated   **B.** aromatic

   C. unbranched   **D.** larger.

3. Which types of hydrocarbons are **not** added to unleaded petrol to improve the efficiency of burning?

   A. branched   **B.** cyclic

   C. aromatic   **D.** unsaturated

4. Which of the following is an example of a reaction which takes place during the process of reforming?

   A. $C_8H_{18} \rightarrow C_4H_8 + C_4H_{10}$

   B. $C_6H_{12} \rightarrow C_6H_6 + 3H_2$

   C. $C_3H_6 + H_2 \rightarrow C_3H_8$

   D. $C_2H_4 + H_2O \rightarrow C_2H_5OH$

5. Which fuel **cannot** be classified as a renewable source of energy?

   A. ethanol   **B.** methane

   C. methanol   **D.** hydrogen

6. Which gas found in car exhaust systems is **not** a result of incomplete combustion?

   A. carbon   **B.** octane

   C. carbon monoxide   **D.** carbon dioxide

7. The burning of which fuel would reduce the build up of carbon dioxide in the atmosphere?

   A. ethanol   **B.** diesel

   C. methane   **D.** hydrogen

8. In nature, carbon is continually being recycled. Part of the cycle is shown below.

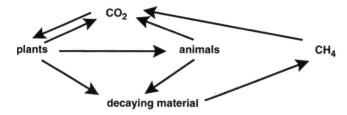

The production of methane from decaying material is due to

A. photosynthesis
B. respiration
C. aerobic conditions
D. anaerobic conditions.

9. Which set of results could be obtained if methanol is analysed by mass?

	Mass of carbon	Mass of hydrogen	Mass of oxygen
A.	3 g	1 g	4 g
B.	3 g	2 g	8 g
C.	6 g	8 g	16 g
D.	12 g	8 g	32 g

10. The tendency of a petrol component to ignite spontaneously is measured by its octane number.

	Compound	Octane number
1	3-methylpentane	74.5
2	pentane	61.7
3	butane	93.6
4	2-methylpentane	73.4
5	hexane	24.8
6	methylcyclopentane	91.3

A pupil made the hypothesis that as the chain length increases, the octane number decreases.

Which set of three components should have their octane numbers compared in order to test this hypothesis?

A. 1, 4, 6   B. 1, 2, 4
C. 2, 3, 5   D. 3, 4, 5

In questions 1 to 12 decide whether each of the hydrocarbons is

A. an alkane   **B.** an alkene   **C.** an alkyne

D. saturated   **E.** unsaturated

(Note that for each question, **two** responses should be given.)

1. ethane

2. cyclopropane

3. propene

4. 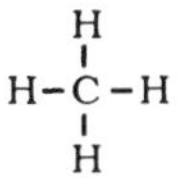
$$H-\underset{\underset{H}{|}}{\overset{\overset{H}{|}}{C}}-H$$

5.

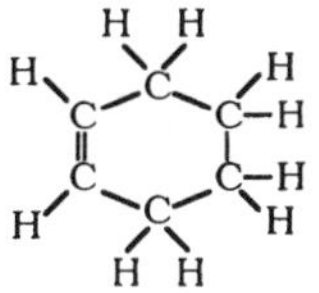

6.

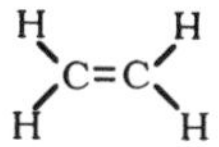

7. propyne

8. cycloheptene

9. octane

10. H-C≡C-H

11.

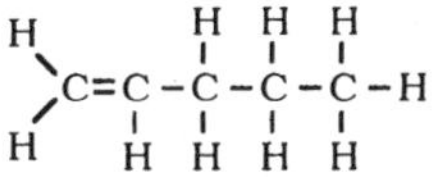

12.

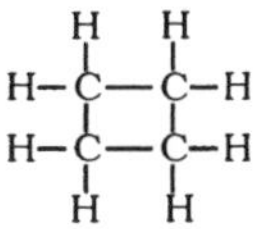

Questions 13 to 18 refer to the naming of hydrocarbons.

A.
```
      H
      |
   H-C-H
      |
      H
```

B.
```
   H         H
    \       /
     C = C
    /       \
   H         H
```

C. $H-C\equiv C-H$

D.
```
   H           H
    \          |
     C = C - C - H
    /        |   |
   H         H   H
```

E.
```
   H  H  H  H
   |  |  |  |
H-C -C -C -C -H
   |  |  |  |
   H  H  H  H
```

F.
```
   H  H  H
   |  |  |
H-C -C -C -H
   |  |  |
   H  H  H
```

G.
```
   H  H  H  H
   |  |  |  |
H-C -C =C -C -H
   |        |
   H        H
```

H.
```
        H  H
         \ /
          C
         / \
   H-C ——— C-H
   H/        \H
```

I.
```
   H   H
   |   |
H-C — C-H
   |   |
H-C — C-H
   |   |
   H   H
```

J.
```
   H       H
    \      |
     C — C-H
     |   |
     C — C-H
    /    |
   H     H
```

13. Which is methane?

14. Which is a butene?

15. Which is ethyne?

16. Which is propene?

17. Which is cyclopropane?

18. Which is cyclobutene?

Questions 19 to 23 refer to the formulae of C_6 hydrocarbons.

A. C_6H_{10} **B.** C_6H_{12} **C.** C_6H_{14}

What is the formula for each of the hydrocarbons?

19. hexane

20. cyclohexane

21. hexene

22. hexyne

23. cyclohexene

24. How many hydrogen atoms are in a straight-chain alkane with 25 carbon atoms?

    A. 48   **B.** 50   **C.** 52   **D.** 54

25. How many hydrogen atoms are in a straight-chain alkene with 12 carbon atoms?

    A. 20   **B.** 22   **C.** 24   **D.** 26

26. How many hydrogen atoms are in a straight-chain alkyne with 4 carbon atoms?

    A. 4   **B.** 6   **C.** 8   **D.** 10

27. How many hydrogen atoms are in a cycloalkane with 16 carbon atoms?

    A. 28   **B.** 30   **C.** 32   **D.** 34

28. How many hydrogen atoms are in a cycloalkene with 21 carbon atoms?

    A. 40   **B.** 42   **C.** 44   **D.** 46

29. Which of the following could **not** be either a straight-chain alkane or a cycloalkane?

    A. C_4H_{10} **B.** C_5H_{10} **C.** C_6H_{12} **D.** C_7H_{12}

In questions 30 to 34 decide which hydrocarbon is **not** a member of the same homologous series as the others.

30. **A.** ethene   **B.** hexene   **C.** butene   **D.** cyclopropane

31. **A.** butane   **B.** methane   **C.** octane   **D.** propyne

32. **A.** C_3H_8 **B.** C_5H_{12} **C.** C_6H_{12} **D.** C_7H_{16}

33. **A.** CH_4 **B.** C_3H_6 **C.** C_6H_{12} **D.** C_8H_{16}

34. Hydrocarbons with a formula mass of :

   A. 16   **B.** 44   **C.** 84   **D.** 100

Questions 35 and 37 refer to homologous series.

   A. CH_4 **B.** $CH_2{=}CH_2$ **C.** $\begin{array}{c} CH_2\text{-}CH_2 \\ |\quad\ | \\ CH_2\text{-}CH_2 \end{array}$ **D.** $CH_3\text{-}C{\equiv}CH$

Which hydrocarbon is a member of the same homologous series as each of the following?

35. $CH_3CH_2CH_3$

36. $CH_3CHCHCH_3$

37. CHCH

Test 2.3   Systematic naming of hydrocarbons

Questions 1 to 18 refer to the systematic naming of hydrocarbons.
Suggested names are shown.

Decide whether the suggested name for each of the hydrocarbons is

A. CORRECT   **B.** INCORRECT.

1.

$$CH_3-\underset{\underset{H}{|}}{\overset{\overset{CH_3}{|}}{C}}-\underset{\underset{H}{|}}{\overset{\overset{CH_3}{|}}{C}}-CH_3$$

2,3-dimethylbutane

2.

$$CH_3-\underset{\underset{\underset{CH_3}{|}}{\overset{|}{CH_2}}}{\overset{\overset{H}{|}}{C}}-CH_2-CH_3$$

2-ethylbutane

3.

$$CH_3-C\equiv C-\underset{\underset{H}{|}}{\overset{\overset{CH_3}{|}}{C}}-CH_3$$

4-methylpent-2-yne

4.

$$H-\underset{\underset{CH_3}{|}}{\overset{\overset{CH_3}{|}}{C}}-CH_2-CH_2-CH_3$$

1,1-dimethylbutane

5.

$$CH_3-\overset{\overset{\overset{H}{\diagdown}\overset{}{C}\overset{}{\diagup}H}{\|}}{C}-CH_2-CH_3$$

2-methylbut-1-ene

6.

$$CH_3-\underset{\underset{CH_3}{|}}{\overset{\overset{H}{|}}{C}}=C-\underset{\underset{H}{|}}{\overset{\overset{CH_3}{|}}{C}}-CH_3$$

2,3-dimethylpent-2-ene

7.

$$\begin{array}{l}CH_2-CH_2\\CH_2-\underset{\underset{CH_3}{|}}{\overset{\overset{}{|}}{C}}-CH_3\end{array}$$

1,1-dimethylcyclobutane

8.

$$H-\underset{\underset{CH_2-CH_3}{|}}{\overset{\overset{H}{|}}{C}}-C\equiv C-H$$

3-ethylprop-1-yne

9. 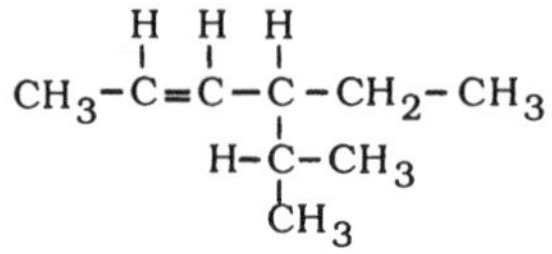
$CH_3-C=C-C-CH_2-CH_3$ with H H H above and $H-C-CH_3$ / CH_3 below

4-ethyl, 5-methylhex-2-ene

10.

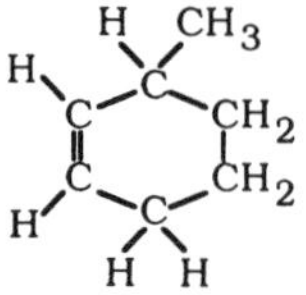

2-methycyclohexene

11. $CH_3CH(CH_3)CH(CH_3)CH_3$ 2,3-dimethylbutane

12. $(CH_3)_3CH$ methylpropane

13. $CH_3CHC(CH_3)_2$ pent-2-ene

14. $CHCCH_3$ propene

15. $CH_3CH_2C(CH_3)_2CH_2CH_3$ 3-ethylpentane

16. $(CH_3)_2CCH_2$ but-1-ene

17. $CH_3C(CH_3)_2CCH$ 3,3-dimethybut-1-yne

18. $CH_3CHCHCH(CH_3)CH_2CH_3$ 3-methyhex-2-ene

19. Which hydrocarbon has a molecular formula different from that of the other three?

    A.   2,2-dimethyl, 3,3-dimethylbutane
    B.   3-ethylpentane
    C.   2,3-dimethylpentane
    D.   2,2-dimethyl, 3-methylbutane

20. Which hydrocarbon has the same formula mass as 3,3-dimethylbut-1-ene?

    A. $CH_3C(CH_3)_2CH_2CH_3$
    B. $CH_2C(CH_3)CH_2CH_3$
    C. $CH_2C(CH_3)CH_2CH_2CH_3$
    D. $CH_3CH(CH_3)CH(CH_3)_2$

(Note that for some of the questions in the test, more than one response may be correct.)

Question 1 to 3 refer to isomers of alkanes.

A. $CH_3- CH_2- CH_2- CH_3$

B. $CH_3- CH_2- CH_2- CH_2- CH_3$

C. $CH_3- CH- CH_2- CH_3$
               $|$
              CH_3

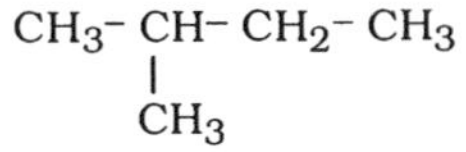

D. $CH_3- CH_2- CH_2- CH_2- CH_2- CH_3$

               CH_3
               $|$
E. $CH_3- CH- CH_3$

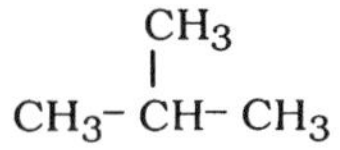

F. CH_3
              $|$
      $CH_3- C- CH_3$
              $|$
              CH_3

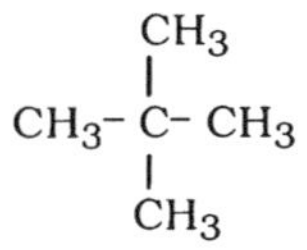

G. CH_3
                           $|$
    $CH_3- CH_2- CH_2- CH- CH_3$

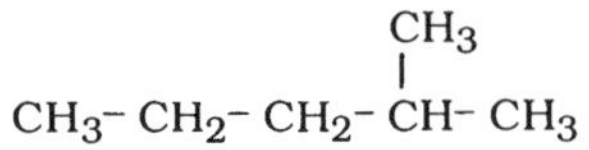

Pick out **all** the compounds that are isomers of each of the structures.

1.   **A**

2.   **B**

3.   **D**

Questions 4 and 5 refer to isomers of alkanes with the formula C_5H_{12}.

A.
```
    H  H  H  H  H
    |  |  |  |  |
H - C -C -C -C -C -H
    |  |  |  |  |
    H  H  H  H  H
```

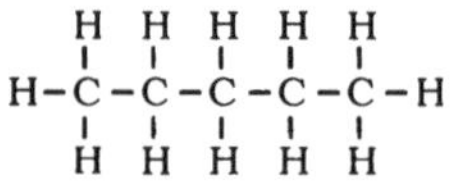

B.
```
    H  H  H
    |  |  |
H - C -C -C -H
    |     |
    H     H
    H - C - H
    |
    H - C - H
        |
        H
```

C.
```
    H  H
    |  |
H - C -C -H
    |  |
    H  H
    |  |
H - C -C -H
    |
    H
    H - C - H
        |
        H
```

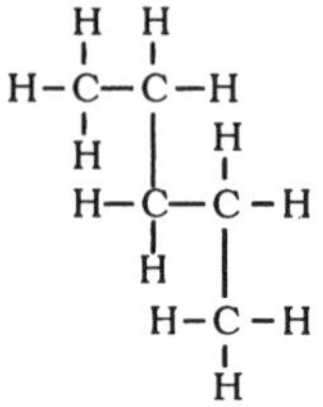

D.
```
        H
        |
    H - C - H
    |       |
    H       H
    |       |
H - C - C - C - H
    |       |
    H       H
    H - C - H
        |
        H
```

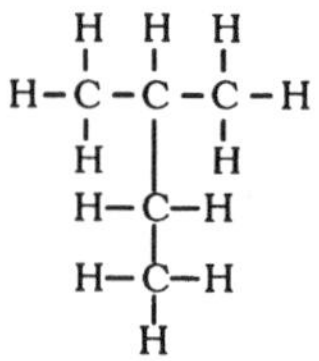

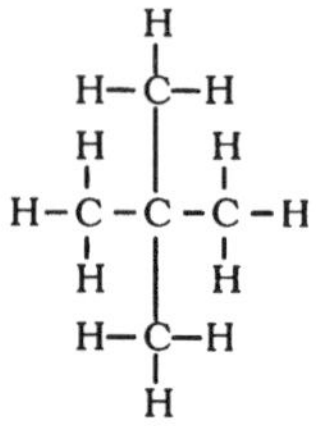

E.
```
        H
        |
    H - C - H
    |       |
    H       H  H
    |       |  |
H - C - C - C - C - H
    |   |   |   |
    H   H   H   H
```

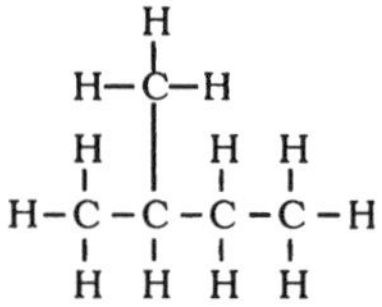

F.
```
    H  H  H  H
    |  |  |  |
H - C -C -C -C -H
    |  |     |
    H  H     H
       H - C - H
           |
           H
```

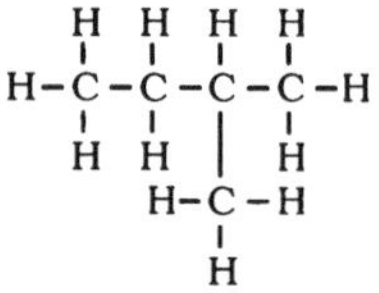

Pick out **all** the compounds that are **not** isomers of each of the structures.

4. **A**

5. **B**

6. Pick out **all** the compounds that are isomers of the following structure.

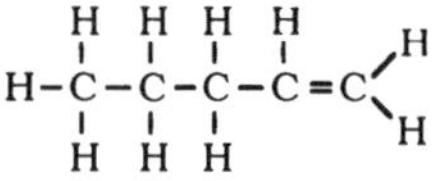

```
    H  H  H  H     H
    |  |  |  |    /
H - C -C -C -C = C
    |  |  |      \
    H  H  H       H
```

A.
(cyclopentane ring structure)

B.
```
H       H  H  H
 \      |  |  |
  C=C - C -C -C -H
 /      |  |  |  |
H       H  H  H  H
```

C.
```
    H  H  H  H  H
    |  |  |  |  |
H = C -C -C -C -C -H
    |  |  |  |  |
    H  H  H  H  H
```

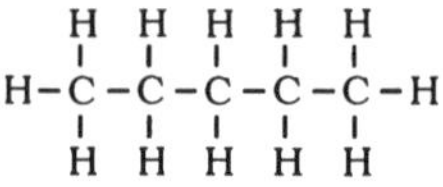

D.
```
    H  H  H  H  H
    |  |  |  |  |
H - C -C =C -C -C -H
    |        |  |
    H        H  H
```

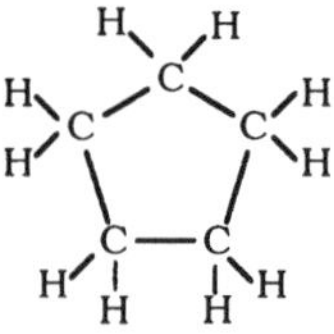

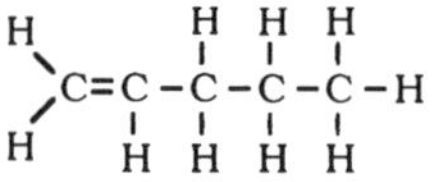

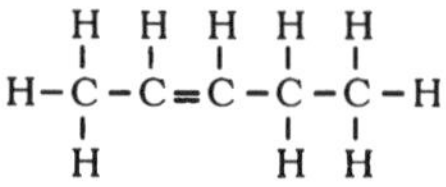

Questions 7 and 8 refer to isomers of alkenes with the formula C_5H_{10}.

A.

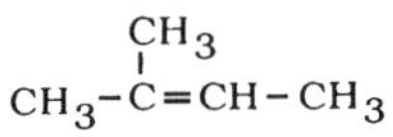

$$CH_3-\underset{\underset{CH_3}{|}}{C}=CH-CH_3$$

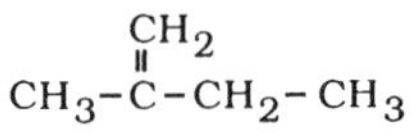

B.

$$CH_3-\underset{\overset{CH_2}{||}}{C}-CH_2-CH_3$$

C.

$$CH_2=\underset{\underset{CH_3}{|}}{C}-CH_2-CH_3$$

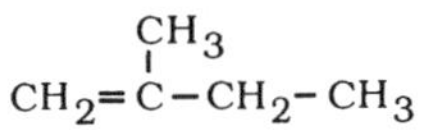

D.

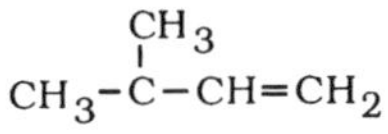

$$CH_3-\underset{\overset{CH_3}{|}}{C}-CH=CH_2$$

E.

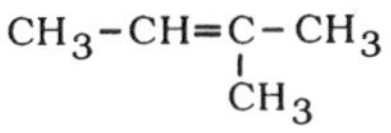

$$CH_3-CH=\underset{\underset{CH_3}{|}}{C}-CH_3$$

F.

$$CH_3-CH_2-\underset{\underset{CH_3}{|}}{C}=CH_2$$

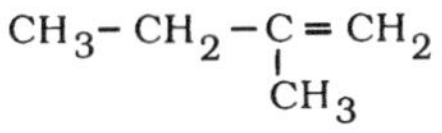

Pick out **all** the compounds that are **not** isomers of each of the structures.

7. **A**

8. **C**

In questions 9 to 16 decide whether each of the pairs of hydrocarbons

A. are isomers	**B.** are **NOT** isomers.

9. 2-methlypentane	and	heptane
10. 2,3-dimethylbutane	and	hexane
11. 2-methylpent-1-ene	and	hexene
12. hexene	and	methylcyclopentane
13. hexyne	and	cyclohexene
14. pentane	and	$CH_3CHCHCH_2CH_3$
15. hexane	and	$CH_3CH(CH_3)CH(CH_3)CH_3$
16. cyclopentane	and	$CH_2C(CH_3)CH_2CH_3$

Test 2.5   Structures of substituted alkanes

The questions in this test refer to oxygen-containing organic compounds.

A.
$$CH_3-\overset{\overset{\textstyle O}{\|}}{C}-CH_3$$

B. CH_3COOH

C. CH_3OH

D. butanone

E. $CH_3-O-\overset{\overset{\textstyle O}{\|}}{C}-H$

F. ethanal

G. CH_3-O-CH_3

H. $H-C\overset{\displaystyle O}{\underset{\displaystyle OH}{}}$

I. $CH_3-CH_2-\overset{\overset{\textstyle O}{\|}}{C}-H$

J. $CH_3COCH_2CH_3$

K. $CH_3-O-\overset{\overset{\textstyle O}{\|}}{C}-CH_3$

L. methanol

M. $H-\overset{\overset{\textstyle O}{\|}}{C}-H$

N. $HCOOCH_2CH_3$

O. CH_3CH_2CHO

P.

Q. $CH_3CH(OH)CH_3$

R.

S.

T.

U.
$$CH_3-\overset{\overset{\textstyle CH_3}{|}}{\underset{\underset{\textstyle CH_3}{|}}{C}}-CH_2-OH$$

V. $CH_3-O-CH_2CH_3$

W.

1. Pick out **all** the compounds which are **alcohols**.

2. Pick out **all** the compounds which are **organic acids**.

3. Pick out **all** the compounds which are **aldehydes**.

4. Pick out **all** the compounds which are **ketones**.

Test 2.6   Simple esters - structures and names

In question 1 to 20 decide whether each of the organic compounds

A. is an ester

B. is **NOT** an ester.

1. methanol

2. ethyl methanoate

3. hexanone

4. butanoic acid

5. methyl propanoate

6. pentanal

7. $CH_3-\overset{\overset{O}{\|}}{C}-O-CH_2\,CH_3$

8. CH_3CH_2OH

9. CH_3-O-CH_3

10. $CH_3-\overset{\overset{O}{\|}}{C}-OH$

11. $CH_3-\overset{\overset{O}{\|}}{C}-CH_3$

12. $CH_3-O-\overset{\overset{O}{\|}}{C}-CH_3$

13. $CH_3-\overset{\overset{O}{\|}}{C}-O-CH_3$

14. $CH_3-\overset{\overset{O}{\|}}{C}-H$

15. $CH_3CH_2COOCH_3$

16. CH_3CH_2COOH

17. $CH_3CH_2CH_2OH$

18. CH_3CH_2CHO

19. CH_3COOCH_3

20. $CH_3CH_2COCH_2CH_3$

Questions 21 to 24 refer to names of esters.

21. What ester is formed in the reaction of methanol with ethanoic acid?

    A. methyl ethanoate   **B.** ethyl methanoate

22. What ester is formed in the reaction of propanol with methanoic acid?

    A. methyl propanoate   **B.** propyl methanoate

23. What ester is formed in the reaction of ethanoic acid with butanol?

    A. butyl ethanoate   **B.** ethyl butanoate

24. What ester is formed in the reaction of butanoic acid with methanol?

    A. butyl methanoate   **B.** methyl butanoate

Questions 25 to 28 refer to structures of esters.

A.

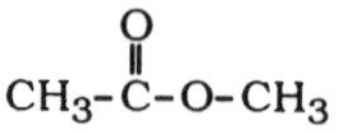

$$CH_3-\overset{\overset{\displaystyle O}{\|}}{C}-O-CH_3$$

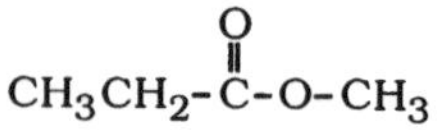

B.

$$CH_3CH_2-\overset{\overset{\displaystyle O}{\|}}{C}-O-CH_3$$

C.

$$CH_3CH_2-O-\overset{\overset{\displaystyle O}{\|}}{C}-CH_3$$

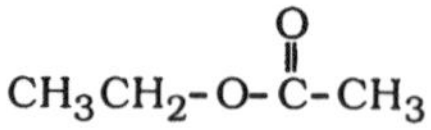

D.

$$CH_3CH_2-O-\overset{\overset{\displaystyle O}{\|}}{C}-H$$

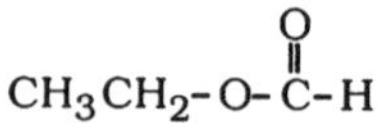

25. What is the structure of the ester formed in the reaction between ethanol and methanoic acid?

26. What is the structure of the ester formed in the reaction between propanoic acid and methanol?

27. What is the structure of ethyl ethanoate?

28. What is the structure of methyl ethanoate?

29. The formulae for the molecules from which ethylbutanoate is made are

    A. C_3H_7OH and CH_3COOH

    B. C_2H_5OH and C_2H_5COOH

    C. C_3H_7COOH and C_2H_5OH

    D. C_2H_5COOH and C_3H_7OH.

In questions 1 to 6 decide whether each of the pairs of compounds

A. are isomers

B. are **NOT** isomers.

1.
$$Br-\underset{\underset{H}{|}}{\overset{\overset{H}{|}}{C}}-\underset{\underset{H}{|}}{\overset{\overset{H}{|}}{C}}-Br$$

and

$$H-\underset{\underset{Br}{|}}{\overset{\overset{H}{|}}{C}}-\underset{\underset{H}{|}}{\overset{\overset{Br}{|}}{C}}-H$$

2.
$$Br-\underset{\underset{H}{|}}{\overset{\overset{H}{|}}{C}}-\underset{\underset{H}{|}}{\overset{\overset{H}{|}}{C}}-Br$$

and

$$H-\underset{\underset{Br}{|}}{\overset{\overset{Br}{|}}{C}}-\underset{\underset{H}{|}}{\overset{\overset{H}{|}}{C}}-H$$

3. $CH_3-CH_2-CH_2-OH$

and

$$CH_3-\underset{\underset{OH}{|}}{\overset{\overset{H}{|}}{C}}-CH_3$$

4.
$$CH_3-\overset{\overset{O}{\|}}{C}-O-CH_3$$

and

$$CH_3-CH_2-\overset{\overset{O}{\|}}{C}-OH$$

5.
$$CH_3-\overset{\overset{O}{\|}}{C}-CH_3$$

and

$$CH_3-CH_2-\overset{\overset{O}{\|}}{C}-OH$$

6.
$$CH_3-CH_2-\overset{\overset{O}{\|}}{C}-H$$

and

$$CH_3-\overset{\overset{O}{\|}}{C}-CH_3$$

Questions 7 to 9 refer to the isomers of oxygen-containing compounds.

A. CH_3COOCH_3

B. $CH_3CH_2CH_2COOH$

C. CH_3COCH_3

D. $CH_3CH_2CH_2CHO$

7. Which compound is an isomer of propanoic acid?

8. Which compound is an isomer of propanal?

9. Which compound is an isomer of butanone?

10. Which ester is an isomer of butanoic acid?

    A.   Ethyl ethanoate
    B.   Ethyl methanoate
    C.   Ethyl propanoate
    D.   Propyl ethanoate

11. Which compound is an isomer of hexanal?

    A.   2-methylbutanal
    B.   3-methylpentan-2-one
    C.   2, 2-dimethylbutan-1-ol
    D.   3-ethylpentanal

In questions 12 to 17 decide whether each of the compounds

    A.   does have an isomeric form
    B.   does **NOT** have an isomeric form.

12. $CH_3CH_2CH_2OH$

13. C_2H_3Cl

14. chloroethane

15. C_3H_7Cl

16. CH_3CHCl_2

17. methanol

In questions 1 to 14 decide whether each of the statements about benzene is

A. TRUE   **B.** FALSE.

1. Benzene is the second member of the series of aromatic hydrocarbons.

2. Benzene contains more elements than hexane.

3. Benzene has the formula C_6H_6.

4. The ratio of carbon atoms to hydrogen atoms in benzene is the same as in ethyne.

5. Benzene behaves towards bromine solution as if unsaturated.

6. Benzene is an isomer of cyclohexane.

7. All the carbon to carbon bonds in benzene are the same length.

8. The stability of the benzene ring is due to the delocalisation of electrons.

9. The phenyl group has the formula - C_6H_4.

10. Only one product is formed when one hydrogen atom is replaced by one chlorine atom.

11. Benzene undergoes addition reactions more readily than hexene.

12. More than one product is formed when two hydrogen atoms are replaced by two chlorine atoms.

13. Benzene is more volatile than ethane.

14. Benzene does **not** react readily with a solution of bromine.

Questions 15 to 17 refer to the formulae for aromatic compounds.

How many hydrogen atoms are present in a molecule of each compound?

15.

aspirin

A. 5   **B.** 7   **C.** 8   **D.** 10

16.

T.C.P.

A. 3   **B.** 4   **C.** 6   **D.** 7

17.

naphthalene

A. 6   **B.** 8   **C.** 10   **D.** 12

Questions 1 to 10 refer to the experiment shown.

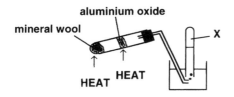

In the apparatus, the mineral wool was soaked with a liquid alkane, $C_{12}H_{26}$. Its vapour was passed over hot aluminium oxide and a gas collected at **X** by displacement of water.

Decide whether each of the statements is

A.   TRUE   **B.**   FALSE.

1. An addition reaction is taking place.

2. The aluminium oxide acts as a catalyst.

3. Only methane gas is produced.

4. The gas collected quickly decolourises bromine.

5. The gas collected could contain ethene.

6. The gas collected turns lime water milky.

7. The gas collected contains a mixture of hydrocarbons.

8. The gas collected contains unsaturated molecules.

9. Molecules with the formula $C_{13}H_{26}$ are found in the gas.

10. The gas collected could contain ethane.

11. A liquid hydrocarbon had no visible effect on bromine, but when it was cracked the gases produced decolourised bromine.

    This is because

    A.   gases decolourise bromine; liquids do not
    B.   some of the gases formed were unsaturated; the liquid was not
    C.   the gases formed were at a higher temperature than the liquid
    D.   some of the gases formed by the cracking were not hydrocarbons.

12. $C_{16}H_{34}$ $\rightarrow$ $C_{10}H_{20}$ + **X**

What is the formula for **X**?

A. C_6H_{14} B. $C_{10}H_{22}$
C. $C_{16}H_{12}$ D. $C_{26}H_{24}$

13. $C_{10}H_{22}$ $\rightarrow$ C_6H_{12} + C_2H_6 + **X**

What is the formula for **X**?

A. methane   B. ethene
C. butane   D. butene

14. Hexane can be cracked to give ethene and another hydrocarbon.

The other hydrocarbon must be

A. propane   B. propene
C. butane   D. butene.

15. A C_{11} alkane is cracked into pentane and two other straight-chain hydrocarbons.

If one of these is ethene, the other must be

A. propane   B. propene
C. butane   D. butene.

16. Which equation could represent an industrial cracking process?

A. $CH_3(CH_2)_6CH_3$ $\rightarrow$ $CH_3(CH_2)_4CH_3$ + $CH_2=CH_2$
B. $CH_3(CH_2)_6CH_2OH$ $\rightarrow$ $CH_3(CH_2)_5CH=CH_2$ + H_2O
C. $CH_3(CH_2)_6CH_3$ $\rightarrow$ $CH_3C(CH_3)_2CH_2CH(CH_3)_2$
D. $4CH_2=CH_2$ $\rightarrow$ $-(CH_2CH_2)_4$-

In questions 17 to 23 decide whether each of the statements is

A. TRUE **B.** FALSE.

17. Ethene and propene can be obtained by the cracking of naphtha.

18. Ethene can be obtained by the cracking of ethane.

19. Propene can be obtained by the cracking of ethane.

20. Propane can be obtained by the cracking of propene.

21. Branched chain alkanes can be obtained by the cracking of propane.

22. Hexene can be obtained by the cracking of ethene.

23. Ethene can be obtained by the cracking of propane.

Test 2.10

Addition reactions

In questions 1 to 12 decide whether each of the hydrocarbons

A. does undergo an addition reaction

B. does **NOT** undergo an addition reaction.

1. octene

2. hexane

3. ethyne

4. pentene

5. cyclopropane

6. cycloheptene

7.
$$
\begin{array}{c}
\text{H} \\
\diagdown \\
\text{H} \diagup
\end{array}
\text{C} = \text{C}
\begin{array}{c}
\diagup \text{H} \\
\diagdown \text{H}
\end{array}
$$

8.
$$
\begin{array}{cc}
\text{H} & \text{H} \\
| & | \\
\text{H}-\text{C}-\text{C}-\text{H} \\
| & | \\
\text{H} & \text{H}
\end{array}
$$

9.
$$
\begin{array}{cc}
\text{H} & \text{H} \\
\text{H}-\text{C}-\text{C}-\text{H} \\
\text{H}-\text{C}-\text{C}-\text{H} \\
\text{H} & \text{H}
\end{array}
$$

10.
$$
\begin{array}{c}
\text{H} \\
| \\
\text{H}-\text{C}-\text{C}\equiv\text{C}-\text{H} \\
| \\
\text{H}
\end{array}
$$

11.
$$
\begin{array}{c}
\text{H} \\
| \\
\text{H}-\text{C}-\text{H} \\
| \\
\text{H}
\end{array}
$$

12.
$$
\begin{array}{c}
\text{H}\quad \text{H} \\
\text{H}\diagdown\quad\diagup\text{C}\diagdown\quad\diagup\text{H} \\
\text{C}\qquad\qquad\text{C}-\text{H} \\
|\qquad\qquad\qquad\text{C}-\text{H} \\
\text{H}\diagup\quad\diagdown\text{C}\diagup\quad\diagdown\text{H} \\
\text{H}\quad \text{H}
\end{array}
$$

(Note that for questions 13 and 14 more than one response is correct.)

13. Which of the following represents the product of the reaction between ethene and bromine?

A.

$$\begin{array}{c} H \\ \\ Br \end{array} C=C \begin{array}{c} H \\ \\ Br \end{array}$$

B.

$$\begin{array}{c} H \quad Br \\ | \quad | \\ H-C-C-Br \\ | \quad | \\ H \quad H \end{array}$$

C.

$$\begin{array}{c} Br \quad Br \\ | \quad | \\ Br-C-C-Br \\ | \quad | \\ Br \quad H \end{array}$$

D.

$$\begin{array}{c} H \quad H \\ | \quad | \\ H-C-C-H \\ | \quad | \\ Br \quad H \end{array}$$

E.

$$\begin{array}{c} Br \quad H \\ | \quad | \\ H-C-C-H \\ | \quad | \\ Br \quad H \end{array}$$

F.

$$\begin{array}{c} H \quad Br \\ | \quad | \\ H-C-C-H \\ | \quad | \\ Br \quad H \end{array}$$

G.

$$\begin{array}{c} Br \quad Br \\ | \quad | \\ Br-C-C-Br \\ | \quad | \\ Br \quad Br \end{array}$$

H.

$$\begin{array}{c} H \quad H \\ | \quad | \\ Br-C-C-Br \\ | \quad | \\ H \quad H \end{array}$$

14. Which of the following represents the product of the reaction between propene and bromine?

A.

$$\begin{array}{c} H \quad H \quad H \\ | \quad | \quad | \\ H-C-C-C-H \\ | \quad | \quad | \\ Br \quad H \quad Br \end{array}$$

B.

$$\begin{array}{c} Br \quad H \quad H \\ | \quad | \quad | \\ Br-C-C-C-H \\ | \quad | \quad | \\ H \quad H \quad H \end{array}$$

C.

$$\begin{array}{c} Br \\ \\ Br \end{array} C=C \begin{array}{c} H \quad H \\ | \quad | \\ -C-H \\ | \\ H \end{array}$$

D.

$$\begin{array}{c} Br \quad H \quad H \\ | \quad | \quad | \\ H-C-C-C-H \\ | \quad | \quad | \\ H \quad Br \quad H \end{array}$$

E.

$$\begin{array}{c} H \\ \\ Br \end{array} C=C \begin{array}{c} Br \quad H \\ | \quad | \\ -C-H \\ | \\ H \end{array}$$

F.

$$\begin{array}{c} H \quad H \quad H \\ | \quad | \quad | \\ H-C-C-C-H \\ | \quad | \quad | \\ Br \quad Br \quad H \end{array}$$

G.

$$\begin{array}{c} H \quad H \quad H \\ | \quad | \quad | \\ Br-C-C-C-Br \\ | \quad | \quad | \\ H \quad H \quad H \end{array}$$

H.

$$\begin{array}{c} H \quad Br \quad H \\ | \quad | \quad | \\ H-C-C-C-Br \\ | \quad | \quad | \\ H \quad H \quad H \end{array}$$

15. A hydrocarbon, molecular formula C_5H_{10}, does **not** quickly decolourise bromine.

    Which hydrocarbon could it be?

    A. pentane   **B.** cyclopentane
    C. pentene   **D.** cyclopentene

16. When a molecule of the compound $CH_2 = CH - CH = CH_2$ completely reacts with bromine, the number of molecules of bromine used would be

    A. 1   **B.** 2   **C.** 3   **D.** 4.

17. What kind of reaction takes place when butene decolourises bromine?

    A. cracking   **B.** addition
    C. oxidation   **D.** condensation

18. What is formed when butene reacts with hydrogen?

    A. ethane   **B.** propane   **C.** butane   **D.** hexane

19. Which hydrocarbon reacts with hydrogen to form hexane?

    A. propene   **B.** pentane   **C.** hexene   **D.** octane

    Questions 20 and 21 refer to the two-stage reaction of ethyne with hydrogen chloride.

20. The product of the first stage is

    A. saturated   **B.** unsaturated.

21. The product of the second stage is

    A. saturated   **B.** unsaturated.

22. What kind of reaction takes place when pentyne reacts with hydrogen?

    A. hydrolysis   **B.** reforming
    C. hydration   **D.** hydrogenation

23. Ethyne can react with bromine in two stages.

What is the full structural formula for the product of the second stage?

A.
$$
\begin{array}{cc}
H & H \\
| & | \\
C & = C \\
| & | \\
Br & Br
\end{array}
$$

B.
$$
\begin{array}{cc}
Br & H \\
| & | \\
C & = C \\
| & | \\
Br & H
\end{array}
$$

C.
$$
\begin{array}{cc}
Br & H \\
| & | \\
H-C & -C-H \\
| & | \\
H & Br
\end{array}
$$

D.
$$
\begin{array}{cc}
Br & Br \\
| & | \\
H-C & -C-H \\
| & | \\
Br & Br
\end{array}
$$

24. Ethyne reacts with chlorine to give an unsaturated product **X**. Product **X** then reacts with hydrogen forming a saturated product **Y**.

What is the full structural formula for product **Y**?

A.
$$
\begin{array}{cc}
Cl & H \\
| & | \\
H-C & -C-H \\
| & | \\
Cl & H
\end{array}
$$

B.
$$
\begin{array}{cc}
Cl & Cl \\
| & | \\
H-C & -C-H \\
| & | \\
H & H
\end{array}
$$

C.
$$
\begin{array}{cc}
Cl & Cl \\
| & | \\
H-C & -C-H \\
| & | \\
Cl & Cl
\end{array}
$$

D.
$$
\begin{array}{cc}
Cl & Cl \\
| & | \\
Cl-C & -C-Cl \\
| & | \\
Cl & Cl
\end{array}
$$

Test 2.11   Reactions involving alkanols

Questions 1 to 7 refer to the experiment shown.

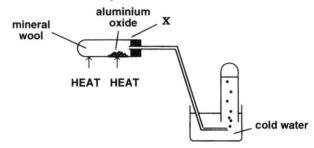

The mineral wool was soaked with an alkanol. The vapour was passed over red-hot aluminium oxide.

1. The reaction taking place in tube **X** is an example of

   A. condensation   **B.** dehydration
   C. dehydrogenation   **D.** hydrolysis.

2. What is the product when ethanol is used in the reaction?

   A. ethane   **B.** ethene
   C. ethanal   **D.** ethanoic acid

3. What is the product when butan-1-ol is used in the reaction?

   A. but-1-ene   **B.** but-2-ene
   C. a mixture of but-1-ene and but-2-ene

4. What is the product when butan-2-ol is used in the reaction?
   A.
        but-1-ene   **B.** but-2-ene
   C. a mixture of but-1-ene and but-2-ene

5. What alkanol will produce pent-2-ene as the only product?

   A. pentan-1-ol   **B.** pentan-2-ol
   C. pentan-3-ol

6. Which alkanol can produce, on dehydration, a pair of isomeric alkenes?

   A. propan-2-ol   **B.** pentan-3-ol
   C. hexan-3-ol   **D.** heptan-4-ol

7. What product(s) would be expected upon dehydration of the following alkanol?

   A. 2-methylbut-2-ene only
   B. 2-methylbut-2-ene and 2-methylbut-1-ene
   C. 2-methylbut-1-ene only
   D. 3-methylbut-1-ene and 2-methylbut-1-ene

8. Ethanol can be made from glucose by

   A. addition   **B.** hydration
   C. condensation   **D.** fermentation.

   Questions 9 and 10 refer to the production of ethanol by means other than from glucose.

9. What name is applied to the type of reaction which takes place?

   A. catalytic cracking   **B.** steam reforming
   C. fractional distillation   **D.** catalytic hydration

10. What is the feedstock in this reaction?

   A. natural gas   **B.** synthesis gas
   C. ethene   **D.** ethane

The questions in this test refer to alcohols.

A.

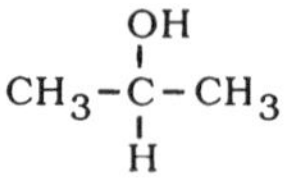

$$CH_3-\underset{\underset{H}{|}}{\overset{\overset{OH}{|}}{C}}-CH_3$$

B.

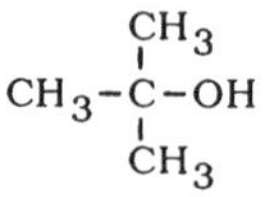

$$CH_3-\underset{\underset{CH_3}{|}}{\overset{\overset{CH_3}{|}}{C}}-OH$$

C. CH_3-OH

D.

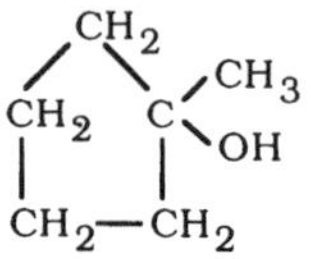

E.

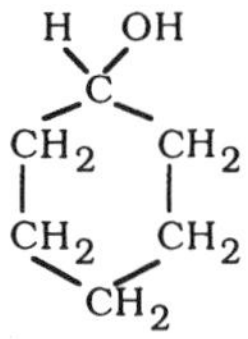

F.

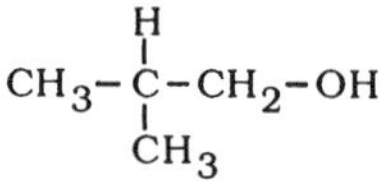

$$CH_3-\underset{\underset{CH_3}{|}}{\overset{\overset{H}{|}}{C}}-CH_2-OH$$

G.

$$CH_3-\underset{\underset{CH_3}{|}}{\overset{\overset{CH_3}{|}}{C}}-CH_2-OH$$

H.

$$CH_3-\underset{\underset{CH_3}{|}}{\overset{\overset{CH_3}{|}}{C}}-\underset{\underset{CH_3}{|}}{\overset{\overset{H}{|}}{C}}-OH$$

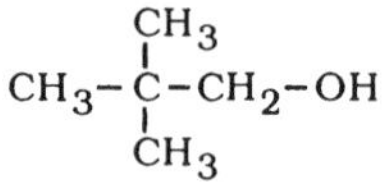

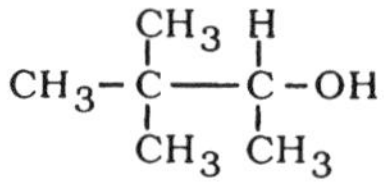

I. $CH_3CH(OH)CH_2CH_3$

J. $CH_3CH_2C(CH_3)_2OH$

K. $CH_3CH(CH_3)CH(CH_3)OH$

L. ethanol

M. hexan-2-ol

N. 2-methylbutan-1-ol

O. 3-methylpentan-2-ol

P. 3-methylhexan-3-ol

1. Pick out **all** the alcohols which are **primary** alcohols.

2. Pick out **all** the alcohols which are **secondary** alcohols.

3. Pick out **all** the alcohols which are **tertiary** alcohols.

In questions 1 to 16 decide whether each of the alcohols can be oxidised to

A. an alkanal   **B.** an alkanone   **C.** neither.

1. CH_3-CH_2-OH

2. $CH_3-CH-CH_3$
   $|$
   OH

3. $CH_3-CH-CH_2-OH$
   $|$
   CH_3

4. CH_3
   $|$
   CH_3-C-OH
   $|$
   CH_3

5. CH_3
   $|$
   CH_3-C-CH_2-OH
   $|$
   CH_3

6. CH_3OH
   $\diagdown C \diagup$
   $CH_2 CH_2$
   $||$
   $CH_2 CH_2$
   CH_2

7. $CH_3CH_2C(CH_3)_2OH$

8. $CH_3CH(CH_3)CH(CH_3)OH$

9. $CH_3CH_2C(CH_3)_2CH_2OH$

10. $CH_3CH(OH)CH_2CH_3$

11. propan-1-ol

12. pentan-3-ol

13. 3-methylpentan-3-ol

14. 2-methylpentan-3-ol

15. 2-methylhexan-1-ol

16. cycloheptanol

In questions 17 to 24 decide whether each of the carbonyl compounds

A. can be easily oxidised to an alkanoic acid.

B. can **NOT** be easily oxidised to an alkanoic acid.

17. ethanal

18. propanone

19. pentanal

20. hexan-2-one

21. $H-C=O$
    $|$
    H

22. $CH_3-CH_2-C-CH_3$
    $||$
    O

23. $CH_3-CH_2-C=O$
    $|$
    H

24. $CH_3-CH_2-C-CH_2-CH_3$
    $||$
    O

Questions 1 to 6 refer to the experiment shown.

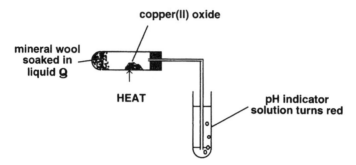

copper(II) oxide

mineral wool soaked in liquid Q

HEAT

pH indicator solution turns red

Decide whether each of the following liquids

   A.   could be liquid **Q**   **B.**   could **NOT** be liquid **Q**.

1. propanone

2. paraffin

3. propanal

4. pentane

5. propan-1-ol

6. propan-2-ol

Questions 7 to 9 refer to the oxidation of carbonyl compounds.

   A.   propanone   **B.**   butanal
   C.   butanone   **D.**   propanal

7. What compound is formed by the oxidation of butan-2-ol?

8. What compound is oxidised to produce $CH_3CH_2CH_2COOH$?

9. What compound is formed by the oxidation of $CH_3CH_2CH_2OH$?

10. When the vapour of a liquid **X** is passed over heated copper(II) oxide, a reaction occurs and the vapour produced gives an orange precipitate with Benedict's solution.

Which of the following could be **X**?

A. propan-1-ol **B.** propan-2-ol
C. propanal **D.** propanone

11. What type of reaction takes place when methanol is converted to methanal?

A. condensation **B.** oxidation
C. hydrolysis **D.** dehydration

12. Propan-1-ol is converted to propanal by warming it with potassium dichromate solution acidified with sulphuric acid.

The function of the acid/dichromate mixture is to

A. reduce the alcohol
B. dehydrate the alcohol
C. hydrate the alcohol
D. oxidise the alcohol.

In questions 13 to 16 decide whether each of the reactions is an example of

A. oxidation **B.** reduction.

13. $C_2H_6O \rightarrow C_2H_4O$

14. $C_7H_6O \rightarrow C_7H_6O_2$

15. $C_6H_{10}O \rightarrow C_6H_{12}O$

16. $CH_2O_2 \rightarrow CH_2O$

17. Which compound will produce a carboxylic acid on oxidation?

A. CH_3OH

B. CH_3CHCH_3 (with OH on the central C)
$\quad\quad\quad |$
$\quad\quad\ OH$

C.
$\quad CH_3$
$\quad\ |$
CH_3CHCH_3
$\quad\ |$
$\quad OH$

D. CH_3CCH_3
$\quad\quad \|$
$\quad\quad O$

18. Bacterial oxidation of a solution of ethanol will result in the production of

   A. ethanoic acid
   B. ethene
   C. ethyl ethanoate
   D. ethane.

19. Oxidation of 4-methylpentan-2-ol to the corresponding ketone results in the molecule

   A. losing 2 g per mole
   B. gaining 2 g per mole
   C. gaining 16 g per mole
   D. not changing in mass.

20. What compound is formed by the oxidation of propan-2-ol?

   A. CH_3CH_2CHO
   B. CH_3COCH_3
   C. CH_3CH_2COOH
   D. $CH_3CH_2CH_2OH$

In questions 1 to 6 decide whether each of the statements about methyl ethanoate is

A. TRUE   **B.** FALSE.

1. It is soluble in water.

2. It has a characteristic smell.

3. It is a conductor of electricity.

4. It is flammable.

5. It is made up of molecules.

6. It turns Universal indicator solution red.

Questions 7 and 8 refer to the reaction of ethanoic acid and an alcohol in the presence of concentrated sulphuric acid.

7. The product is

     A. a hydrocarbon   **B.** an ester
     C. a salt   **D.** a carbohydrate.

8. The reaction can be considered to be an example of

     A. precipitation   **B.** distillation
     C. condensation   **D.** neutralisation.

9. The formation of ethanol from ethyl ethanoate is an example of

     A. condensation   **B.** dehydration
     C. hydration   **D.** hydrolysis.

10. Two flasks, **X** and **Y**, with their contents as shown, were placed in a vessel of water at 40 °C.

water at 40 °C

methanol + ethanoic acid
+ concentrated sulphuric acid

methyl ethanoate + water
+ concentrated sulphuric acid

After several hours the contents of both flasks were analysed.

Which of the following would be expected?

A. Flask **X** contains methyl ethanoate, methanol and ethanoic acid; flask **Y** is unchanged.

B. Flask **X** and flask **Y** both contain methyl ethanoate, methanol and ethanoic acid.

C. Flask **X** contains methyl ethanoate; flask **Y** is unchanged.

D. Flask **X** contains methyl ethanoate; flask **Y** contains methyl ethanoate, methanol and ethanoic acid.

11. What are the names of the alcohol and the acid produced on hydrolysis of the ester below?

$$CH_3\text{-}\overset{\overset{\textstyle O}{\|}}{C}\text{-}O\text{-}\underset{\underset{\textstyle CH_3}{|}}{CH}\text{-}CH_3$$

A. methanoic acid and propan-1-ol

B. ethanoic acid and propan-1-ol

C. methanoic acid and propan-2-ol

D. ethanoic acid and propan-2-ol

The questions in this test refer to types of reaction.

A.	addition	**B.**	hydration	**C.**	condensation
D.	oxidation	**E.**	hydrogenation	**F.**	hydrolysis
G.	dehydration	**H.**	dehydrogenation	**I.**	reduction

What type of reaction is each of the following?

(Note that for some of the questions more than one response may be correct.)

1. ethene → ethane

2. propan-2-ol → propene

3. methanol → methanal

4. propene → propanol

5. butanal → butan-1-ol

6. butan-2-ol → butanone

7. propane → propene

8. ethanal → ethanoic acid

9. methyl ethanoate → methanol + ethanoic acid

10. ethyne → ethene

11. $CH_3CH(OH)CH_3$ → CH_3COCH_3

12. CH_3CHCH_2 → $CH_3CHClCH_2Cl$

13. CH_3CH_2OH → CH_3CHO

14. CH_3CH_2COOH → CH_3CH_2CHO

15. CH_3CH_2OH → CH_2CH_2

16. HCHO → HCOOH

17. $HCOOH + CH_3OH$ → $HCOOCH_3$

18. CHCH → $CHCl_2CHCl_2$

19. CH_3CH_3 → CH_2CH_2

20. CH_2CH_2 → CH_3CH_2OH

1. $N_2(g) + 3H_2(g) \rightarrow 2NH_3(g)$

   Under test conditions 10 kg of hydrogen reacts with excess nitrogen to produce 6.5 kg of ammonia.

   Calculate the percentage yield.

   A. 10.0   **B.** 11.5   **C.** 13.0   **D.** 14.5

2. $2SO_2(g) + O_2(g) \rightarrow 2SO_3(g)$

   Under test conditions, 2 kg of sulphur dioxide reacts with excess oxygen to produce 0.5 kg of sulphur trioxide.

   Calculate the percentage yield.

   A. 20   **B.** 25   **C.** 30   **D.** 40

3. $C_2H_4 + H_2O \rightarrow CH_3CH_2OH$
   ethene   ethanol

   Under test conditions, 2.0 kg of ethanol is obtained from 1.5 kg of ethene.

   Calculate the percentage yield.

   A. 75.3   **B.** 77.3   **C.** 79.3   **D.** 81.3

4. propan-2-ol $\xrightarrow{\text{oxidation}}$ propanone
   $CH_3CH(OH)CH_3$ CH_3COCH_3

   In a preparation, 6.4 g of propanone is obtained from 8.0 g of propan-2-ol.

   Calculate the percentage yield.

   A. 82.8   **B.** 84.0   **C.** 85.2   **D.** 86.4

5. ethanol   +   methanoic acid $\rightarrow$ ethyl methanoate
   CH_3CH_2OH HCOOH $HCOOCH_2CH_3$

   In a preparation, 37 g of ethyl methanoate is obtained from 28.3 g of ethanol.

   Calculate the percentage yield.

   A. 77.3   **B.** 79.3   **C.** 81.3   **D.** 83.3

Questions 1 to 4 refer to the production of feedstocks for the menufacture of plastics (addition polymers).

1. What type of reaction is used to produce ethene from ethane?

   A. addition   **B.** cracking
   C. hydrogenation   **D.** oxidation

2. Which fraction from crude oil can be used to produce ethene and propene?

   A. naphtha   **B.** kerosine   **C.** diesel   **D.** bitumen

3. Which hydrocarbon can be produced from ethane?

   A. ethene   **B.** propene   **C.** butane   **D.** hexane

4. Which hydrocarbon **cannot** be produced from propane?

   A. methane   **B.** ethene   **C.** propene   **D.** butane

In questions 5 to 16 decide whether each of the molecules

   A. is able to undergo addition polymerisation
   B. is **NOT** able to undergo addition polymerisation.

5.
$$\begin{array}{cc} H & H \\ \diagdown & \diagup \\ C=C \\ \diagup & \diagdown \\ H & H \end{array}$$

6.
$$\begin{array}{cccc} H & H & H & H \\ | & | & | & | \\ H-C-C-C-C-H \\ | & | & | & | \\ H & H & H & H \end{array}$$

7.
$$\begin{array}{cc} H & H \\ \diagdown & | \\ C=C-C-H \\ \diagup & | \ | \\ H & H \ H \end{array}$$

8.
$$\begin{array}{cc} H & H \\ | & | \\ Cl-C-C-Cl \\ | & | \\ H & H \end{array}$$

9. ethane

10. propene

11. octane

12. styrene

13. C_3H_8

14. C_2F_4

15. $C_2H_4Br_2$

16. $CH_3CHCHCl$

Questions 17 to 20 refer to the part of the polymer shown.

17. How many repeating units are in the part of the polymer?

   A. 2   **B.** 3   **C.** 6   **D.** 9

18. What is the repeating unit?

   A.

   $$-\overset{\underset{|}{H}}{\underset{H}{C}}-\overset{\underset{|}{H}}{\underset{H}{C}}-$$

   B.

   $$-\overset{\underset{|}{CH_3}}{\underset{H}{C}}-\overset{\underset{|}{H}}{\underset{H}{C}}-$$

   C.

   $$\overset{\underset{|}{CH_3}}{\underset{H}{C}}=\overset{\underset{|}{H}}{\underset{H}{C}}$$

   D.

   $$-\overset{\underset{|}{H}}{\underset{H}{C}}-\overset{\underset{|}{CH_3}}{\underset{H}{C}}-\overset{\underset{|}{H}}{\underset{H}{C}}-$$

19. What is the name of the monomer?

   A. ethene   **B.** propane   **C.** propene   **D.** butane

20. What is the name of the polymer?

   A. polythene   **B.** poly(propene)
   C. poly(butene)   **D.** P.V.C.

21. Polyvinyl chloride is a polymer of vinyl chloride, $CH_2 = CHCl$ (chloroethene).

   Which of the following is part of the formula for polyvinyl chloride?

   A.

   $$-\overset{\underset{|}{Cl}}{\underset{H}{C}}-\overset{\underset{|}{Cl}}{\underset{H}{C}}-\overset{\underset{|}{Cl}}{\underset{H}{C}}-\overset{\underset{|}{Cl}}{\underset{H}{C}}-$$

   B.

   $$-\overset{\underset{|}{H}}{\underset{Cl}{C}}-\overset{\underset{|}{Cl}}{\underset{H}{C}}-\overset{\underset{|}{H}}{\underset{Cl}{C}}-\overset{\underset{|}{Cl}}{\underset{H}{C}}-$$

   C.

   $$-\overset{\underset{|}{H}}{\underset{H}{C}}-\overset{\underset{|}{Cl}}{\underset{H}{C}}-\overset{\underset{|}{H}}{\underset{H}{C}}-\overset{\underset{|}{Cl}}{\underset{H}{C}}-$$

   D.

   $$-\overset{\underset{|}{H}}{\underset{H}{C}}=\overset{\underset{|}{Cl}}{C}-\overset{\underset{|}{H}}{\underset{H}{C}}=\overset{\underset{|}{Cl}}{C}-$$

22. Acrilan is an addition polymer of acrylonitrile. The structure of acrylonitrile is:

Which of the following is part of the structure for Acrilan?

A.

B.

C.

D.

23. Which monomer could polymerise to give the polymer shown?

A.

B.

C.

D.

24. Which monomer could polymerise to give the polymer shown?

A.

B.

C.

D.

25. Part of a polymer molecule is represented below.

$$-\underset{\underset{H}{|}}{\overset{\overset{CH_3}{|}}{C}}-\underset{\underset{CH_3}{|}}{\overset{\overset{H}{|}}{C}}-\underset{\underset{H}{|}}{\overset{\overset{CH_3}{|}}{C}}-\underset{\underset{CH_3}{|}}{\overset{\overset{H}{|}}{C}}-\underset{\underset{H}{|}}{\overset{\overset{CH_3}{|}}{C}}-\underset{\underset{CH_3}{|}}{\overset{\overset{H}{|}}{C}}-\underset{\underset{H}{|}}{\overset{\overset{CH_3}{|}}{C}}-\underset{\underset{CH_3}{|}}{\overset{\overset{H}{|}}{C}}-$$

The monomer which gives rise to this polymer is

A. but-1-ene
B. but-2-ene
C. methylpropene
D. propene.

26. Part of a polymer molecule is shown.

$$-\underset{\underset{H}{|}}{\overset{\overset{CH_3}{|}}{C}}-\underset{\underset{H}{|}}{\overset{\overset{H}{|}}{C}}-\underset{\underset{H}{|}}{\overset{\overset{H}{|}}{C}}-\underset{\underset{H}{|}}{\overset{\overset{H}{|}}{C}}-\underset{\underset{H}{|}}{\overset{\overset{CH_3}{|}}{C}}-\underset{\underset{H}{|}}{\overset{\overset{H}{|}}{C}}-\underset{\underset{H}{|}}{\overset{\overset{H}{|}}{C}}-\underset{\underset{H}{|}}{\overset{\overset{H}{|}}{C}}-$$

Which pair of alkenes was used as monomers?

A. ethene and propene
B. ethene and but-1-ene
C. propene and but-1-ene
D. ethene and but-2-ene

Condensation polymers

In questions 1 to 13 decide whether each of the polymers is made by

A. addition polymerisation   **B.** condensation polymerisation.

1. polythene

2. polystyrene

3. bakelite

4. perspex

5. nylon

6. P.V.C.

7. formica

8. poly(butene)

9. $-CH_2-CH-CH_2-CH-CH_2-CH-$
  $\qquad\;\; CH_3 \qquad\quad CH_3 \qquad\quad CH_3$

10. $-\overset{O}{\overset{\|}{C}}-\overset{H}{\overset{|}{N}}-(CH_2)_6-\overset{H}{\overset{|}{N}}-\overset{O}{\overset{\|}{C}}-(CH_2)_4-\overset{O}{\overset{\|}{C}}-\overset{H}{\overset{|}{N}}-(CH_2)_6-\overset{H}{\overset{|}{N}}-\overset{O}{\overset{\|}{C}}-$

11. $-\overset{F}{\overset{|}{\underset{F}{\overset{|}{C}}}}-\overset{F}{\overset{|}{\underset{F}{\overset{|}{C}}}}-\overset{F}{\overset{|}{\underset{F}{\overset{|}{C}}}}-\overset{F}{\overset{|}{\underset{F}{\overset{|}{C}}}}-\overset{F}{\overset{|}{\underset{F}{\overset{|}{C}}}}-\overset{F}{\overset{|}{\underset{F}{\overset{|}{C}}}}-$

12. $-CH_2-CH-CH_2-CH-CH_2-CH-$
  $\qquad\;\; CN \qquad\quad CN \qquad\quad CN$

13. $-\overset{O}{\overset{\|}{C}}-O-(CH_2)_2-O-\overset{O}{\overset{\|}{C}}-(CH_2)_6-\overset{O}{\overset{\|}{C}}-O-(CH_2)_2-O-$

Questions 14 and 15 refer to nylon. Part of the polymer chain is shown.

$$-\overset{\displaystyle O}{\overset{\|}{C}}-(CH_2)_4-\overset{\displaystyle O}{\overset{\|}{C}}-\overset{\displaystyle H}{\overset{|}{N}}-(CH_2)_4-\overset{\displaystyle H}{\overset{|}{N}}-\overset{\displaystyle O}{\overset{\|}{C}}-(CH_2)_4-\overset{\displaystyle O}{\overset{\|}{C}}-\overset{\displaystyle H}{\overset{|}{N}}-(CH_2)_4-\overset{\displaystyle H}{\overset{|}{N}}-$$

14. How many repeating units are in the part of the polymer shown?

    A.   1   **B.**   2   **C.**   3   **D.**   4

15. Which is (are) the monomers unit(s)?

   A.

$$HO-\overset{\displaystyle O}{\overset{\|}{C}}-(CH_2)_4-\overset{\displaystyle O}{\overset{\|}{C}}-\overset{\displaystyle N}{\overset{|}{N}}-(CH_2)_4-\overset{\displaystyle H}{\overset{|}{N}}-H$$

   B.

$$HO-\overset{\displaystyle O}{\overset{\|}{C}}-(CH_2)_4-\overset{\displaystyle H}{\overset{|}{N}}-H$$

   C.

$$HO-\overset{\displaystyle O}{\overset{\|}{C}}-(CH_2)_4-\overset{\displaystyle O}{\overset{\|}{C}}-OH \qquad H-\overset{\displaystyle N}{\overset{|}{N}}-(CH_2)_4-\overset{\displaystyle H}{\overset{|}{N}}-H$$

   D.

$$H-\overset{\displaystyle O}{\overset{\|}{C}}-(CH_2)_4-\overset{\displaystyle O}{\overset{\|}{C}}-H \qquad HO-\overset{\displaystyle N}{\overset{|}{N}}-(CH_2)_4-\overset{\displaystyle H}{\overset{|}{N}}-OH$$

16. A condensation polymer is made from the monomer shown.

$$H-\overset{\displaystyle H}{\overset{|}{N}}-\overset{\displaystyle CH_3}{\underset{\displaystyle H}{\overset{|}{\underset{|}{C}}}}-\overset{\displaystyle O}{\overset{\|}{C}}-OH$$

Which of the following is part of the polymer chain?

   A.

$$-\overset{\displaystyle H}{\overset{|}{N}}-\overset{\displaystyle CH_3}{\underset{\displaystyle H}{\overset{|}{\underset{|}{C}}}}-\overset{\displaystyle H}{\overset{|}{N}}-\overset{\displaystyle O}{\overset{\|}{C}}-\overset{\displaystyle CH_3}{\underset{\displaystyle H}{\overset{|}{\underset{|}{C}}}}-\overset{\displaystyle O}{\overset{\|}{C}}-$$

   B.

$$-\overset{\displaystyle H}{\overset{|}{N}}-\overset{\displaystyle CH_3}{\underset{\displaystyle H}{\overset{|}{\underset{|}{C}}}}-\overset{\displaystyle}{\underset{\displaystyle OH}{\overset{}{C}}}-\overset{\displaystyle H}{\overset{|}{N}}-\overset{\displaystyle CH_3}{\underset{\displaystyle H}{\overset{|}{\underset{|}{C}}}}-\overset{\displaystyle}{\underset{\displaystyle OH}{\overset{}{C}}}-$$

   C.

$$-\overset{\displaystyle}{\overset{}{N}}-\overset{\displaystyle CH_3}{\underset{\displaystyle H}{\overset{|}{\underset{|}{C}}}}-\overset{\displaystyle H}{\overset{|}{C}}-\overset{\displaystyle O}{\overset{\|}{C}}-\overset{\displaystyle}{\overset{}{N}}-\overset{\displaystyle CH_3}{\underset{\displaystyle H}{\overset{|}{\underset{|}{C}}}}-\overset{\displaystyle H}{\overset{|}{C}}-\overset{\displaystyle O}{\overset{\|}{C}}-$$

   D.

$$-\overset{\displaystyle H}{\overset{|}{N}}-\overset{\displaystyle CH_3}{\underset{\displaystyle H}{\overset{|}{\underset{|}{C}}}}-\overset{\displaystyle O}{\overset{\|}{C}}-\overset{\displaystyle H}{\overset{|}{N}}-\overset{\displaystyle CH_3}{\underset{\displaystyle H}{\overset{|}{\underset{|}{C}}}}-\overset{\displaystyle O}{\overset{\|}{C}}-$$

17. The following monomers can be used to prepare nylon–6,6.

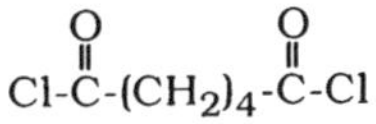

$$\underset{\text{Cl-C-(CH}_2)_4\text{-C-Cl}}{\overset{O \qquad\quad O}{\Vert \qquad\quad \Vert}} \qquad\qquad H_2N\text{-(CH}_2)_6\text{-NH}_2$$

Which molecule is released during the condensation reaction between these monomers?

A.	HCl	**B.**	H_2O
C.	NH_3	**D.**	HOCl

18. Which structure shows an amide link?

A. 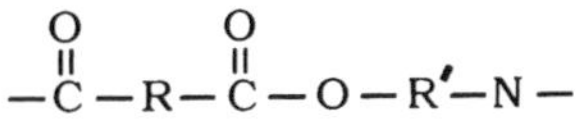
$$\underset{-C-R-C-O-R'-N-}{\overset{O \qquad O}{\Vert \qquad \Vert}}$$

B. 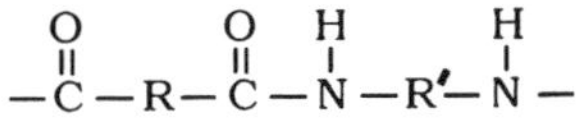
$$\underset{-C-R-C-N-R'-N-}{\overset{O \qquad O\ \ H \qquad\ \ H}{\Vert \qquad \Vert\ \ |\qquad\quad\ |}}$$

C.
$$-O-R-O-R'-O-$$

D. 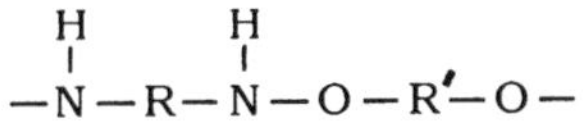
$$\underset{-N-R-N-O-R'-O-}{\overset{H\qquad\ \ H}{|\qquad\quad |}}$$

19. Part of a polymer chain is shown.

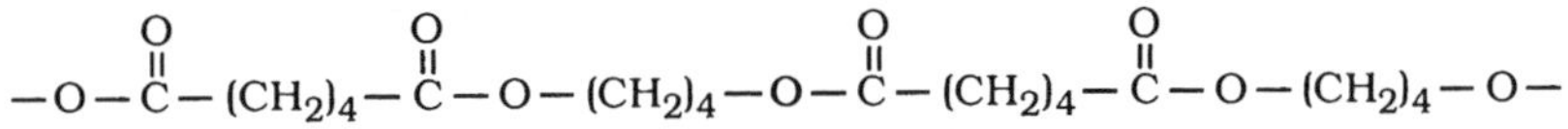

$$-O-\underset{}{\overset{O}{\overset{\Vert}{C}}}-(CH_2)_4-\overset{O}{\overset{\Vert}{C}}-O-(CH_2)_4-O-\overset{O}{\overset{\Vert}{C}}-(CH_2)_4-\overset{O}{\overset{\Vert}{C}}-O-(CH_2)_4-O-$$

Which compound, when added to the reactants during polymerisation, would stop the polymer chain from getting too long?

A. 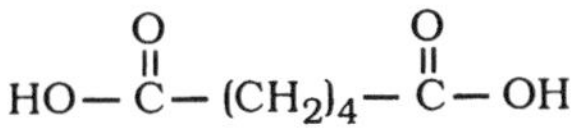 $\quad HO-\overset{O}{\overset{\Vert}{C}}-(CH_2)_4-\overset{O}{\overset{\Vert}{C}}-OH$

B. $\quad HO-(CH_2)_6-OH$

C. 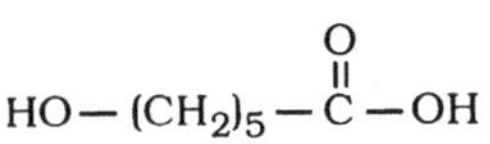 $\quad HO-(CH_2)_5-\overset{O}{\overset{\Vert}{C}}-OH$

D. $\quad CH_3-OH$

Test 2.20

In questions 1 to 4 decide whether each of the following

   A. is used to produce synthesis gas
   B. is **NOT** used to produce synthesis gas.

1. petrol

2. coal

3. crude oil

4. methane

5. Which of the following processes is used to produce synthesis gas?

   A. steam reforming   **B.** fractional distillation
   C. catalytic cracking   **D.** direct oxidation

6. Synthesis gas can be made by

   A. fractional distillation of liquid air
   B. burning coal in excess air
   C. burning natural gas in a limited supply of air
   D. reacting natural gas with steam.

In questions 7 to 12 decide whether each of the gases

   A. is a component of synthesis gas
   B. is **NOT** a component of synthesis gas.

7. carbon dioxide

8. oxygen

9. hydrogen

10. ethene

11. carbon monoxide

12. methane

13. Which of the following is directly made from synthesis gas?

   A. ethanol   **B.** ethene   **C.** methanol   **D.** methane

14. Methanal can be produced from methanol by

   A. cracking   **B.** addition   **C.** reforming   **D.** oxidation.

15. Methanal is widely used

   A. as a fuel   **B.** as a solvent
   C. to make thermoplastics   **D.** to make thermosetting plastics.

Test 2.21

Recently developed polymers

The questions in this test refer to the following polymers.

A. poly(ethenol)   **B.** poly(ethene)   **C.** poly(ethyne)

D. Biopol   **E.** Kevlar   **F.** polyvinylcarbazole

1. Which polymer is soluble in water?

2. Which polymer is biodegradable?

3. Which polymer is used to replace steel because of its great strength?

4. Which polymer is used to make the membrane for high-performance loud speakers?

5. Which polymer has a low density form which can be used to produce a photodegradable polymer?

6. Which polymer exhibits photoconductivity?

7. Which polymer has a structure similar to that of nylon?

8. Which polymer is used to make disposable laundry bags?

9. Which polymer is made from another plastic by a process known as ester exchange?

10. Which polymer consists of 'sheets' of polymer chains held together by hydrogen bonds?

In questions 1 to 5 decide whether each of the statements is

A. TRUE

B. FALSE.

1. Fats and oils in the diet supply the body with energy.

2. Carbohydrates are a more concentrated source of energy than fats and oils.

3. Fats are likely to have relatively low melting points compared to oils.

4. Oils have a higher degree of unsaturation than fats.

5. Molecules in fats are packed more closely together than in oils.

6. Fats and oils can be classified as

A.	carbohydrates	**B.**	acids
C.	esters	**D.**	alcohols.

7. The breakdown of fats and oils produces glycerol and

A.	acids	**B.**	alkanes
C.	alkenes	**D.**	esters.

8. What is the structural formula for glycerol?

A.
$$CH_2OH$$
$$|$$
$$CHOH$$
$$|$$
$$CH_2OH$$

B.
$$CH_2OH$$
$$|$$
$$CH_2$$
$$|$$
$$CH_2OH$$

C.
$$CH_2OH$$
$$|$$
$$CH_2OH$$

D.
$$CH_2OH$$
$$|$$
$$CHOH$$
$$|$$
$$CH_2COOH$$

9. Glycerol can be obtained from a fat by

A.	oxidation	**B.**	condensation
C.	hydrolysis	**D.**	esterification.

10. The breakdown of fats and oils produces glycerol and fatty acids in the ratio of

A.	one mole to one mole	**B.**	one mole to two mole
C.	one mole to three mole	**D.**	one mole to four mole.

11. What type of reaction is represented by the following equation?

$$
\begin{array}{c}
CH_2-O-\overset{\overset{O}{\|}}{C}-C_{17}H_{35} \\
CH-O-\overset{\overset{O}{\|}}{C}-C_{17}H_{35} \\
CH_2-O-\overset{\overset{O}{\|}}{C}-C_{17}H_{35}
\end{array}
\; + \; 3H_2O \; \rightarrow \;
\begin{array}{c}
CH_2-OH \\
CH-OH \\
CH_2-OH
\end{array}
\; + \; 3C_{17}H_{35}COOH
$$

A.	condensation	**B.**	hydrolysis
C.	oxidation	**D.**	dehydration

12. The conversion of linoleic acid, $C_{18}H_{32}O_2$, into stearic acid, $C_{18}H_{36}O_2$, is likely to be achieved by

A.	hydrogenation	**B.**	hydrolysis
C.	hydration	**D.**	dehydrogenation.

13. A vegetable oil is mixed with hydrogen under pressure at about 200 °C in the presence of a catalyst.

The hydrogen

A.	dissolves in the oil without reacting
B.	combines with oxygen in the oil
C.	makes the unsaturated oil saturated
D.	makes the oil polymerise.

Questions 14 and 16 refer to kinds of reaction.

A.	hydrolysis	**B.**	dehydration
C.	hydrogenation	**D.**	condensation

14. What kind of reaction takes place during the breakdown of fats during digestion?

15. What kind of reaction takes place during the process by which some liquid oils can be converted into solid fats?

16. What kind of reaction takes place during the production of soap from fats and oils?

17. In the formation of 'hardened' fats from vegetable oil, the hydrogen

   A. causes cross-linking between chains
   B. causes hydrolysis to occur
   C. increases the carbon chain length
   D. reduces the number of carbon-carbon double bonds.

18. Fats have higher melting points than oils because comparing fats and oils

   A. fats have more hydrogen bonds
   B. fats have stronger van der Waals's forces between molecules
   C. fat molecules are more loosely packed
   D. fat molecules are more unsaturated.

19. Which of the following decolourises bromine solution least rapidly?

   A. palm oil
   B. hex-1-ene
   C. cod liver oil
   D. mutton fat

Test 2.23   Proteins

1. Proteins are substances which, in addition to carbon, hydrogen and
   oxygen, always contain

   A. phosphorus   **B.** nitrogen
   C. sulphur   **D.** calcium.

2.
$$H-\underset{\underset{CH_3}{|}}{\overset{\overset{CH_3}{|}}{C}}-\underset{\underset{H}{|}}{\overset{\overset{NH_2}{|}}{C}}-C\overset{O}{\underset{OH}{}}$$

   The molecule can be classified as

   A. an amino acid   **B.** an ester
   C. a peptide   **D.** a protein.

   Questions 3 and 4 refer to the breakdown of protein during digestion to give
   smaller molecules.

3. Which compound might be obtained by the breakdown of protein?

   A. glucose   **B.** glycerol
   C. stearic acid   **D.** amino-ethanoic acid

4. What name can be given to the type of reaction which takes place?

   A. dehydration   **B.** condensation
   C. hydrogenation   **D.** hydrolysis

5. Proteins can be denatured under acid conditions.

   During this process, the protein molecule

   A. changes shape   **B.** is dehydrated
   C. is neutralised   **D.** is polymerised.

6. In which kind of compound is nitrogen always present?

   A. enzymes   **B.** oils
   C. polyesters   **D.** carbohydrates

7. Which nitrogen containing compound could be a starting material for protein synthesis?

   A. $Pb(NO_3)_2$
   B. $(NH_4)_2SO_4$
   C. $H_2N(CH_2)_4NH_2$
   D. $(CH_3)_2C(NH_2)COOH$

8. What type of chemical reaction takes place in the formation of proteins from amino acids?

   A. condensation
   B. hydration
   C. hydrolysis
   D. dehydration

9. Which of the following could represent part of a protein structure?

   A.

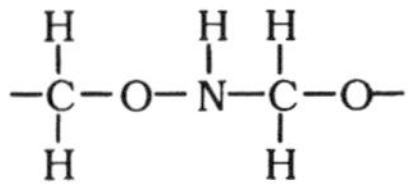

   B.

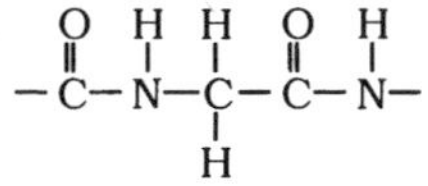

   C.

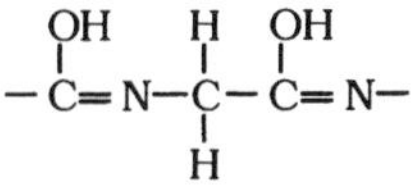

   D.

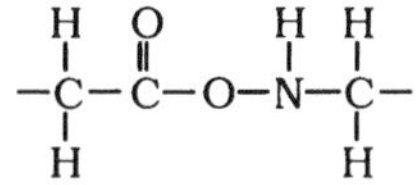

10. When two amino acids join together a peptide link is formed.

    Which of the following represents this process?

    A.

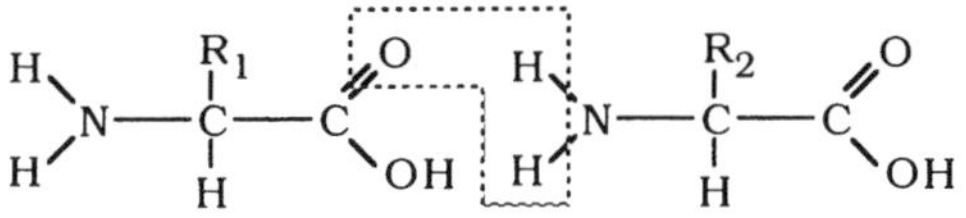

    B.

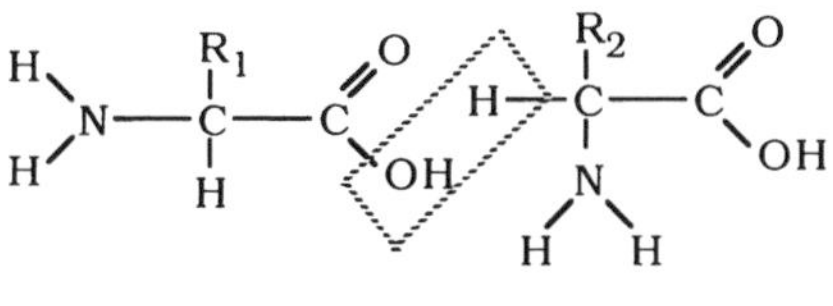

    C.

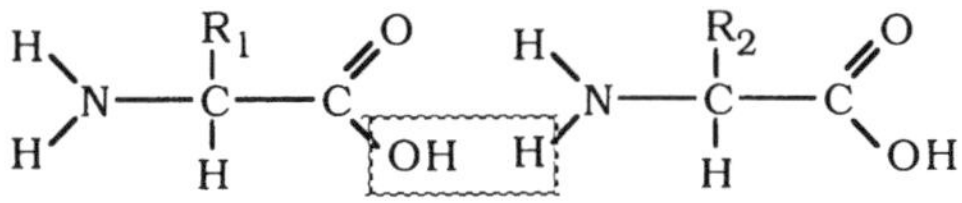

    D.

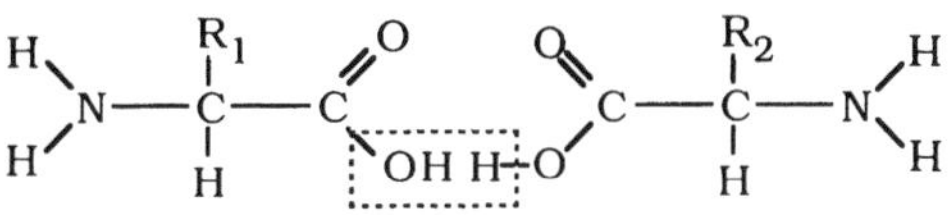

11. Which of the following is the most likely optimum temperature for human enzyme activity?

A. close to 20 °C   B. close to 40 °C

C. close to 60 °C   D. close to 80 °C

12. The monomer units used to construct enzyme molecules are

A. esters   B. amino acids
C. fatty acids   D. monosaccharides

13. Some amino acids have the amino group on the carbon atom adjacent to the acid group. These are called α-amino acids.

Which of the following is an a-amino acid?

A. $CH_2 — CH — COOH$ B. $CH_3 — CH — COOH$
  $\ \ \ |\ \ \ \ \ \ \ |$ $\ \ \ \ \ \ \ \ \ \ \ \ \ \ |$
  $\ \ \ SH\ \ \ \ NH_2$ $\ \ \ \ \ \ \ \ \ \ \ \ \ \ CH_2 — NH_2$

C.

D.

14. The graph shows how the rate of reaction varies with pH.

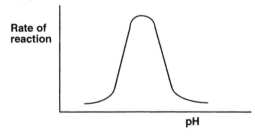

Which reaction could produce this graph?

A. the fermentation of sucrose
B. neutralisation of an acid by an alkali
C. the combustion of sucrose
D. the reaction of a metal with acid

15.   The rate of hydrolysis of a protein, using an enzyme, was studied
       at different temperatures.

Which graph could be obtained?

A.

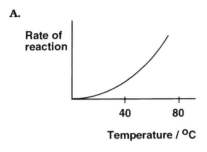

B.

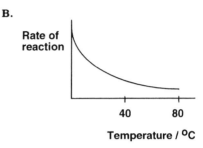

C.

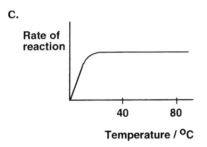

D.

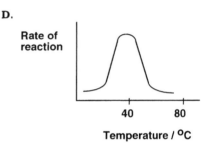

In questions 16 to 20 decide whether each statement refers to

A.   fibrous proteins   **B.**   globular proteins.

16.   made of spiral chains folded into compact units

17.   have a long and thin structure

18.   are the major structural materials of skin and hair

19.   make up many hormones

20.   make up enzymes

Test 3.1   The chemical industry

Questions 1 to 5 refer to the costs involved in the chemical industry.

Decide whether each of the following is most likely to be classified as

A.   a fixed cost   **B.**   a variable cost.

1. the cost of land rental

2. the cost of plant construction

3. the cost of product distribution

4. the cost of labour

5. the cost of raw materials

Questions 6 to 16 refer to feedstocks in the chemical industry.

Decide whether each feedstock

A.   can be classified as a raw material
B.   cannot be classified as a raw material.

6. air	12. iron ore
7. propane	13. water
8. coal	14. benzene
9. sodium chloride	15. sulphuric acid
10. ammonium nitrate	16. methane
11. polystyrene	

Questions 17 to 20 refer to ways of organising chemical production.

Decide whether each product would be manufactured by

A.   a continuous process   **B.**   a batch process.

17. sulphuric acid

18. aspirin

19. ammonia

20. DDT (a pesticide)

Test 3.2   Hess's Law

1. Given the equations:

$$Mg_{(s)} \quad + \quad 2H^+_{(aq)} \quad \rightarrow \quad Mg^{2+}_{(aq)} \quad + \; H_{2(g)} \quad \Delta H \; = \; \mathbf{a}$$
$$Zn_{(s)} \quad + \quad 2H^+_{(aq)} \quad \rightarrow \quad Zn^{2+}_{(aq)} \quad + \; H_{2(g)} \quad \Delta H \; = \; \mathbf{b}$$
$$Mg_{(s)} \quad + \quad Zn^{2+}_{(aq)} \quad \rightarrow \quad Mg^{2+}_{(aq)} \quad + \; Zn_{(s)} \quad \Delta H \; = \; \mathbf{c}$$

then according to Hess's Law

A. $\mathbf{a} + \mathbf{b} = \text{-}\mathbf{c}$ B. $\mathbf{a} + \mathbf{b} = \mathbf{c}$
C. $\mathbf{a} + \mathbf{c} = \mathbf{b}$ D. $\mathbf{a} - \mathbf{b} = \mathbf{c}$.

2. What is the relationship between $\mathbf{a}$, $\mathbf{b}$, $\mathbf{c}$ and $\mathbf{d}$?

$$S_{(s)} \quad + \quad H_{2(g)} \quad \rightarrow \quad H_2S_{(g)} \quad\quad\quad \Delta H = \mathbf{a}$$
$$H_{2(g)} \quad + \quad {}^1/_2 O_{2(g)} \quad \rightarrow \quad H_2O_{(l)} \quad\quad\quad \Delta H = \mathbf{b}$$
$$S_{(s)} \quad + \quad O_{2(g)} \quad \rightarrow \quad SO_{2(g)} \quad\quad\quad \Delta H = \mathbf{c}$$
$$H_2S_{(g)} \quad + \quad 1\,{}^1/_2 O_{2(g)} \quad \rightarrow \quad H_2O_{(l)} \quad + \quad SO_{2(g)} \quad \Delta H = \mathbf{d}$$

A. $\mathbf{a} = \mathbf{b} + \mathbf{c} - \mathbf{d}$ B. $\mathbf{a} = \mathbf{d} - \mathbf{b} - \mathbf{c}$
C. $\mathbf{a} = \mathbf{b} - \mathbf{c} - \mathbf{d}$ D. $\mathbf{a} = \mathbf{d} + \mathbf{c} - \mathbf{b}$

3. The enthalpies of combustion of $C_{(s)}$, $H_{2(g)}$ and $C_4H_9OH_{(l)}$ are:

$$C_{(s)} \quad + \quad O_{2(g)} \quad \rightarrow \quad CO_{2(g)} \quad\quad\quad \Delta H \; = \; \mathbf{a}$$
$$H_{2(g)} \quad + \quad {}^1/_2 O_{2(g)} \quad \rightarrow \quad H_2O_{(l)} \quad\quad\quad \Delta H \; = \; \mathbf{b}$$
$$C_4H_9OH_{(l)} \quad + \quad 6O_{2(g)} \quad \rightarrow \quad 4CO_{2(g)} \; + \quad 5\,H_2O_{(l)} \quad \Delta H \; = \; \mathbf{c}$$

The enthalpy of formation of butanol is the enthalpy change for the reaction:

$$4C_{(s)} \quad + \quad 5H_{2(g)} \quad + \quad {}^1/_2 O_{2(g)} \quad \rightarrow \quad C_4H_9OH_{(l)}$$

What is the enthalpy of formation of butanol?

A. $4\mathbf{a} + 5\mathbf{b} - \mathbf{c}$ B. $2\mathbf{a} + 10\mathbf{b} - \mathbf{c}$
C. $\mathbf{c} - 4\mathbf{a} - 5\mathbf{b}$ D. $2\mathbf{a} + 5\mathbf{b} + \mathbf{c}$

4. Given that the enthalpies of combustion of carbon, hydrogen and ethane are **X**, **Y** and **Z** respectively, the enthalpy change for the reaction

$$2C(s) \quad + \quad 3H_2(g) \quad \rightarrow \quad C_2H_6(g)$$

will be

A. $(2X + 3Y - Z)$ B. $(2X + 3Y + Z)$

C. $(X + Y - Z)$ D. $(-2X - 3Y + Z)$.

5. The enthalpies of combustion for ethene and ethane are ΔH_1 and ΔH_2 respectively.

Given the equations

$$2C(s) \quad + \quad 2H_2(g) \quad \rightarrow \quad C_2H_4(g) \quad \Delta H_3$$

$$2C(s) \quad + \quad 3H_2(g) \quad \rightarrow \quad C_2H_6(g) \quad \Delta H_4$$

the enthalpy change for the reaction

$$C_2H_4(g) \quad + \quad H_2(g) \quad \rightarrow \quad C_2H_6(g) \quad \text{is}$$

A. $\Delta H_1 - \Delta H_2$ B. $\Delta H_2 - \Delta H_1$

C. $\Delta H_3 - \Delta H_4$ D. $\Delta H_4 - \Delta H_3$.

6. $C(s) \quad + \quad O_2(g) \quad \rightarrow \quad CO_2(g) \qquad \Delta H = -395 \text{ kJ mol}^{-1}$

   $CO(g) \quad + \quad {}^1/_2O_2(g) \quad \rightarrow \quad CO_2(g) \qquad \Delta H = -282 \text{ kJ mol}^{-1}$

The enthalpy change for the reaction

$$C(s) \quad + \quad {}^1/_2O_2(g) \quad \rightarrow \quad CO(g)$$

will be

A. $+113$ B. -677 C. -113 D. -197.5

7. Consider the reaction pathway shown.

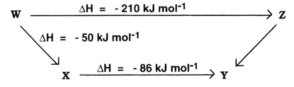

According to Hess's Law, the ΔH value, in kJ mol^{-1}, for reaction **Z** to **Y** is

A. 74 B. -74 C. $+346$ D. -346.

8. $N_2(g)$ + $2O_2(g)$ → $2NO_2(g)$ $\Delta H = +88$ kJ mol^{-1}

      $N_2(g)$ + $2O_2(g)$ → $N_2O_4(g)$ $\Delta H = +10$ kJ mol^{-1}

The enthalpy change, in kJ mol^{-1}, for the reaction

        $2NO_2(g)$ → $N_2O_4(g)$

will be

A.   +98   **B.**   +78   **C.**   -78   **D.**   -98 .

9. What is the enthalpy, in kJ mol^{-1}, for the complete hydrogenation of one mole of ethyne, C_2H_2 ?

(Use the information in the data booklet on enthalpies of combustion.)

A.   -312   **B.**   -26   **C.**   +3146   **D.**   +3432

10. $2Fe(s)$ + $1^1/_2O_2(g)$ → $Fe_2O_3(s)$ $\Delta H = -827$ kJ mol^{-1}

     $2Al(s)$ + $1^1/_2O_2(g)$ → $Al_2O_3(s)$ $\Delta H = -1676$ kJ mol^{-1}

The enthalpy change, in kJ mol^{-1}, for the reaction

      $Fe_2O_3(s)$ + $2Al(s)$ → $2Fe(s)$ + $Al_2O_3(s)$

is given by

A.   -827 + 1676   **B.**   2(-827 + 1676)

C.   +827-1676   **D.** $^1/_2$ (827 - 1676).

11. $CH_2Cl_2(g)$ + $O_2(g)$ → $CO_2(g) + 2HCl(g)$ $\Delta H = -446$ kJ mol^{-1}

     $C(s)$ + $O_2(g)$ → $CO_2(g)$ $\Delta H = -395$ kJ mol^{-1}

     $H_2(g)$ + $Cl_2(g)$ → $2HCl(g)$ $\Delta H = -92$ kJ mol^{-1}

The enthalpy change, in kJ mol^{-1}, for the reaction

$C(s)$ + $H_2(g)$ + $Cl_2(g)$ → $CH_2Cl_2(g)$

will be

A.   -133   **B.**   -41   **C.**   +143   **D.**   +749.

12. $6C(s)$ + $5H_2(g)$ → $C_6H_{10}(l)$ $\Delta H = -3$ kJ mol l^{-1}

      $6C(s)$ + $6H_2(g)$ → $C_6H_{12}(l)$ $\Delta H = +129$ mol l^{-1}

The enthalpy of hydrogenation of cyclohexene to cyclohexane, in kJ mol l^{-1}, will be

A.   -132   **B.**   -129   **C.**   +129   **D.**   +132.

Test 3.3   Equilibrium (i)

The questions in this test refer to reversible reactions at equilibrium.

Decide whether each of the statements is

A. TRUE   **B.** FALSE.

1. The concentrations of reactants are always equal to the concentrations of products.

2. The concentrations of reactants and products are constant.

3. Molecules of reactants are no longer changing into molecules of products.

4. The rates of forward and reverse reactions are equal.

5. The activation energies of the forward and reverse reactions are equal.

6. Catalysts decrease the time required for the equilibrium to be established.

7. Catalysts alter the position of equilibrium.

8. Catalysts lower the activation energy of the forward reactions.

9. Catalysts increase the rate of the reverse reactions.

10. Catalysts increase the activation energy of the reverse reactions.

Decide whether each of the following

A. influences the position of equilibrium
B. does **NOT** influence the position of equilibrium.

11. particle size

12. reactant concentration

13. catalytic action

14. temperature change

Questions 1 to 3 refer to the equilibrium :

$$N_{2(g)} + 3H_{2(g)} \rightleftharpoons 2NH_{3(g)}$$

Changing the concentration of reactants and products can

A. move the equilibrium to the right

B. move the equilibrium to the left.

Decide how the equilibrium mixture would be affected by each of the changes.

1. increasing the concentration of nitrogen gas

2. decreasing the concentration of hydrogen gas

3. decreasing the concentration of ammonia gas

Questions 4 to 9 refer to the equilibrium:

$$Cl_{2(aq)} + H_2O_{(g)} \rightleftharpoons 2H^+_{(aq)} + ClO^-_{(aq)} + Cl^-_{(aq)}$$

The addition of substances can

A. move the equilibrium to the product side

B. move the equilibrium to the reactant side

C. leave the equilibrium mixture unchanged.

Decide the effect of adding each of the substances.

4. sodium chloride crystals

5. nitric acid

6. potassium sulphate crystals

7. silver nitrate solution

8. sodium hydroxide solution

9. potassium nitrate solution

Questions 10 to 15 refer to the effect of an increase in pressure on chemical reactions at equilibrium.

An increase in pressure can

A. increase the concentration of reactants
B. increase the concentration of products
C. have no effect on the concentration of reactants and products.

Decide the effect of an increase in pressure in each of the reactions.

10. $N_2O_4(g) \rightleftharpoons 2NO_2(g)$

11. $H_2(g) + I_2(g) \rightleftharpoons 2HI(g)$

12. $2SO_2(g) + O_2(g) \rightleftharpoons 2SO_3(g)$

13. $NH_3(g) + H_2O(g) \rightleftharpoons NH_4^+(aq) + OH^-(aq)$

14. $CO(g) + H_2O(g) \rightleftharpoons CO_2(g) + H_2(g)$

15. $C(s) + H_2O(g) \rightleftharpoons H_2(g) + CO(g)$

Questions 16 to 19 refer to the effect of a change in temperature on chemical reactions at equilibrium.

A change in temperature can

A. increase the concentration of reactants
B. increase the concentration of products.

What will be the effect of the temperature change in each of the reactions.

16. temperature increase
$PCl_5(g) \rightleftharpoons PCl_3(g) + Cl_2(g)$ $\Delta H = -92 \text{ kJ mol}^{-1}$

17. temperature decrease
$2NO(g) \rightleftharpoons N_2(g) + O_2(g)$ $\Delta H = -180 \text{ kJ mol}^{-1}$

18. temperature increase
$H_2O(g) \rightleftharpoons 2H_2(g) + O_2(g)$ $\Delta H = +484 \text{ kJ mol}^{-1}$

19. temperature decrease
$KBr(s) + (aq) \rightleftharpoons K^+(aq) + Br^-(aq)$ $\Delta H = +20 \text{ kJ mol}^{-1}$

1. 0.1 mol of methanol, 0.1 mol of ethanoic acid and a few drops of concentrated sulphuric acid were warmed together. After a considerable time the reaction mixture was found still to contain some of each of the reactants as well as some ester.

    What is the best explanation of the incomplete reaction?

    A. An equilibrium mixture was formed.
    B. The temperature was too low.
    C. Insufficient methanol was used.
    D. Insufficient catalyst was used.

2. Hydrogen and iodine at 500 °C react according to the equation:

    $$H_2(g) \quad + \quad I_2(g) \quad \rightleftharpoons \quad 2HI(g)$$

    Vessel **X** initially contains 1 mol H_2 + 1 mol I_2; vessel **Y** initially contains 2 mol HI.
    X and **Y** are left at 500 °C until no further change occurs.

    Which statement is then true?

    A. **X** will contain more hydrogen than **Y**.
    B. **X** will contain less iodine than **Y**.
    C. **X** and **Y** will contain the same amount of hydrogen iodide.
    D. **Y** will contain 1 mol of iodine.

    Questions 3 and 4 refer to the addition of compounds to the equilibrium:

    $$Ag^+(aq) \quad + \quad Fe^{2+}(aq) \quad \rightleftharpoons \quad Ag(s) \quad + \quad Fe^{3+}(aq)$$

A. hydrochloric acid	**B.** iron(III) hydroxide
C. iron(II) sulphate	**D.** sulphuric acid

3. Which compound when added to the equilibrium mixture, would lead to an increase in the mass of silver deposited?

4. Which compound when added to the equilibrium mixture, would lead more silver dissolving?

5. $C_2H_4(g)$ + $H_2(g)$ $\rightleftharpoons$ $C_2H_6(g)$ ΔH is -ve

Which procedure would not affect the position of equilibrium?

A. decreasing the pressure
B. decreasing the temperature
C. adding a catalyst
D. adding more hydrogen

6. $2SO_2(g)$ + $O_2(g)$ $\rightleftharpoons$ $2SO_3(g)$

In the presence of a catalyst the equilibrium yield would be

A. increased and attained more rapidly
B. increased and attained in the same time
C. unchanged but attained more rapidly
D. decreased but attained more rapidly.

Questions 7 and 8 refer to reactions at equilibrium.

A. $2CO(g)$ + $O_2(g)$ $\rightleftharpoons$ $CO_2(g)$
B. $H_2(g)$ + $Cl_2(g)$ $\rightleftharpoons$ $2HCl(g)$
C. $PCl_5(g)$ $\rightleftharpoons$ $PCl_3(g)$ + $Cl_2(g)$
D. $2NO_2(g)$ $\rightleftharpoons$ $N_2O_4(g)$

7. For which reaction will the proportion of product present at equilibrium be increased as the pressure is lowered?

8. For which reaction will the equilibrium be unaffected by a change in pressure?

Questions 9 and 10 refer to the most favourable conditions for reactions.

A. high temperature, high pressure
B. high temperature, low pressure
C. low temperature, high pressure
D. low temperature, low pressure

9. $2NO(g)$ + $O_2(g)$ $\rightleftharpoons$ $2NO_2(g)$ ΔH = -560 kJ mol^{-1}

Which conditions favour the formation of NO_2?

10. $CH_4(g)$ + $H_2O(g)$ $\rightleftharpoons$ $CO(g)$ + $3H_2(g)$ ΔH = +206 kJ mol^{-1}

Which conditions favour the formation of hydrogen?

11. The reaction represented by the equation is exothermic.

$$3H_{2(g)} + N_{2(g)} \rightleftharpoons 2NH_{3(g)}$$

In the presence of the appropriate catalyst which set of conditions would give the best yield of ammonia at equilibrium?

A. 800 atmospheres and 2000 ^{o}C
B. 1 atmosphere and 2000 ^{o}C
C. 1 atmosphere and 500 ^{o}C
D. 800 atmospheres and 500 ^{o}C

12. Which entry in the table shows the effect of a catalyst on the reaction rates and position of equilibrium in a reversible reaction?

	Rate of forward reaction	Rate of reverse reaction	Position of equilibrium
A.	increased	increased	unchanged
B.	increased	unchanged	changed
C.	increased	decreased	changed
D.	unchanged	unchanged	unchanged

13. Excess sodium chloride was shaken with water, giving a saturated solution with some solid sodium chloride on the bottom of the container.

$$NaCl_{(s)} \rightleftharpoons Na^{+}_{(aq)} + Cl^{-}_{(aq)}$$

What will happen if $HCl_{(g)}$ is passed through the solution?

A. Chlorine gas will form.
B. The pH will rise.
C. Some sodium chloride will crystallise out.
D. Some solid sodium chloride will dissolve.

14. The decomposition of magnesium carbonate by heat can be prevented from going to completion by

A. absorbing the carbon dioxide produced in lime water
B. removing magnesium oxide as it is formed
C. carrying out the reaction in a small, closed vessel
D. reducing the pressure in the reaction vessel.

Test 3.6

In questions 1 to 12 decide whether each of the statements is

A.   TRUE   **B.**   FALSE.

1.   pH 2 contains more $H^+(aq)$ than $OH^-(aq)$.

2.   pH 6 contains more $H^+(aq)$ than pH 4.

3.   pH 5 contains $H^+(aq)$ but **no** $OH^-(aq)$.

4.   pH 10 contains more $OH^-(aq)$ than $H^+(aq)$.

5.   pH 11 contains **both** $H^+(aq)$ and $OH^-(aq)$.

6.   pH 9 contains more $OH^-(aq)$ than pH 11.

7.   pH 7 contains more $H^+(aq)$ than $OH^-(aq)$.

8.   pH 6 contains an equal concentration of $H^+(aq)$ and $OH^-(aq)$.

9.   pH 4 is more acidic than pH 6.

10.   pH 8 is more alkaline than pH 10.

11.   An acid can have a pH value of 3.8.

12.   An alkali can have a pH value of 10.4.

In questions 13 to 20 decide the pH value of each of the solutions.

A. -1   **B.** 0   **C.** 1   **D.** 4   **E.** 9   **F.** 12   **G.** 14   **H.** 15

13.   0.1 mol l^{-1} hydrochloric acid

14.   0.0001 mol l^{-1} nitric acid

15.   0.01 mol l^{-1} sodium hydroxide solution

16.   0.00001 mol l^{-1} potassium hydroxide solution

17.   1 mol l^{-1} hydrochloric acid

18.   1 mol l^{-1} sodium hydroxide solution

19.   10 mol l^{-1} potassium hydroxide solution

20.   10 mol l^{-1} nitric acid

In questions 21 to 23 decide the concentration of hydrogen ions, in mol l^{-1}, in each of the solutions.

A. 10^{14} **B.** 1   **C.** 10^{-4} **D.** 10^{-5} **E.** 10^{-7} **F.** 10^{-10}

21. pH 5

22. pH 7

23. pH 10

In questions 24 to 26 decide the concentration of hydroxide ions, in mol l^{-1}, in each of the solutions.

A. 10^{-1} **B.** 10^{-4} **C.** 10^{-7} **D.** 10^{-10} **E.** 10^{-13}

24. pH 4

25. pH 7

26. pH 13

27. The pH of a solution of hydrochloric acid was found to be 2.5.

The concentration of the H^{+}(aq) ions in the acid must be

A. greater than 0.1 mol l^{-1}
B. between 0.1 and 0.01 mol l^{-1}
C. between 0.01 and 0.001 mol l^{-1}
D. less than 0.001 mol l^{-1}

28. Raising the pH of a solution from 4 to 6 causes the concentration of the H^{+}(aq) ions to

A. increase by a factor of 2
B. increase by a factor of 100
C. decrease by a factor of 2
D. decrease by a factor of 100.

29. Lowering the pH of a solution from 13 to 10 causes the concentration of the OH^{-}(aq) ions to

A. increase by a factor of 3
B. increase by a factor of 1000
C. decrease by a factor of 3
D. decrease by a factor of 1000.

Questions 1 to 15 refer to the pH of solutions.

A. less than 7   **B.** equal to 7   **C.** more than 7

What is the pH of an aqueous solution of each of the substances?

1. hydrogen chloride
2. ammonia
3. sulphur dioxide
4. carbon dioxide
5. methylamine
6. sodium chloride
7. ammonium nitrate
8. lithium sulphate
9. potassium ethanoate
10. ammonium chloride
11. sodium sulphite
12. potassium carbonate
13. magnesium nitrate
14. sodium tartrate
15. barium chloride

Test 3.8   Strong and weak acids and bases

Questions 1 to 6 refer to equal volumes of 0.1 mol l^{-1} hydrochloric acid and 0.1 mol l^{-1} ethanoic acid.

Decide whether each of the statements is

A. TRUE   **B.** FALSE .

1. They give the same colour with Universal indicator

2. They have a pH less than 7.

3. They conduct electricity equally well.

4. They have equal concentrations of hydrogen ions.

5. They react at the same rate with magnesium.

6. They neutralise the same number of moles of sodium hydroxide.

Questions 7 and 8 refer to 0.1 mol l^{-1} acidic solutions.

A. hydrochloric acid   **B.** ethanoic acid
C. sulphuric acid   **D.** nitric acid

7. Which solution has the lowest electrical conductivity?

8. Which solution has the highest pH?

9. The conductivity of 1 mol l^{-1} nitric acid is higher than the conductivity of 1 mol l^{-1} ethanoic acid.

This is because

A. nitric acid is a concentrated acid
B. ethanoic acid contains more water molecules
C. ethanoic acid is a dilute acid
D. nitric acid contains more H^{+}(aq) ions.

10. Which statement is **not** true of sulphuric, nitric, hydrochloric and ethanoic acid?

A. They react with magnesium.
B. They are completely dissociated in aqueous solution.
C. They react with alkalis.
D. In aqueous solution they have a pH less than 7.

Questions 11 and 12 refer to statements about acids.

A. a weak solution of a strong acid
B. a strong solution of a weak acid
C. a dilute solution of a weak acid
D. a dilute solution of a strong acid.

11. Which statement is applied to 0.1 mol l⁻¹ ethanoic acid?

12. Which statement is applied to 0.1 mol l⁻¹ hydrochloric acid?

13. A fully dissociated acid is progressively diluted by the addition of water.

Which of the following would increase with increasing dilution?

A. the pH value
B. the electrical conductivity
C. the rate of its reaction with chalk
D. the volume of alkali which it will neutralise.

14. Ethanoic acid is referred to as a weak acid because in water

A. there is a partial ionisation of the O-H bonds
B. it has a pH of about 4
C. it is not very soluble
D. it produces only one $H^+_{(aq)}$ ion per molecule.

15. Excess calcium carbonate was added to 100 cm³ of 1 mol l⁻¹ hydrochloric acid. The experiment was repeated using the same mass of the calcium carbonate and 100 cm³ of 1 mol l⁻¹ ethanoic acid.

Which of the following would have been the same for both experiments?

A. the time taken for the reaction to be completed
B. the rate at which the first 10 cm³ of gas is evolved
C. the mass of marble chips left over when reaction has stopped
D. the average rate of reaction

Questions 16 to 20 refer to equal volumes of 0.1 mol l^{-1} sodium hydroxide solution and 0.1 mol l^{-1} ammonia solution.

Decide whether each of the statements is

A. TRUE **B.** FALSE.

16. They give the same colour with Universal indicator.

17. They conduct electricity equally well.

18. They have a pH greater than 7.

19. They contain equal numbers of hydroxide ions.

20. They neutralise the same number of moles of hydrochloric acid.

Questions 21 and 22 refer to 0.1 mol l^{-1} alkaline solutions.

A.	sodium hydroxide	**B.**	ammonium hydroxide
C.	potassium hydroxide	**D.**	lithium hydroxide

21. Which solution has the lowest pH?

22. Which solution has the lowest electrical conductivity?

23. When a certain aqueous solution is diluted, its electrical conductivity decreases but its pH remains constant.

It could be

A. ethanoic acid
B. sodium chloride
C. sodium hydroxide
D. nitric acid.

Oxidation and reduction

In questions 1 to 12 decide whether each of the reactions involve

    A.   oxidation   **B.**   reduction.

You may find it helpful to use the data booklet for questions in this test.

1. $Mg^{2+}(aq) + 2e^- \rightarrow Mg(s)$

2. $Ag(s) \rightarrow Ag^+(aq) + e^-$

3. $2Cl^-(aq) \rightarrow Cl_2(aq) + 2e^-$

4. $Fe^{2+}(aq) + 2e^- \rightarrow Fe(s)$

5. $2I^-(aq) \rightarrow I_2(aq)$

6. $Cu(s) \rightarrow Cu^{2+}(aq)$

7. $SO_3^{2-}(aq) \rightarrow SO_4^{2-}(aq)$

8. $MnO_4^-(aq) \rightarrow Mn^{2+}(aq)$

9. iron(II) $\rightarrow$ iron(III)

10. cobalt(III) $\rightarrow$ cobalt(II)

11. zinc atoms $\rightarrow$ zinc ions

12. bromine molecules $\rightarrow$ bromide ions

In questions 13 to 18 decide whether each of the underlined reactants is acting as

    A.   an oxidising agent   **B.**   a reducing agent

13. $\underline{Zn}(s) + 2H^+(aq) \rightarrow Zn^{2+}(aq) + H_2(g)$

14. $\underline{Cl_2}(aq) + 2I^-(aq) \rightarrow 2Cl^-(aq) + I_2(aq)$

15. $\underline{Mg}(s) + Cu^{2+}(aq) \rightarrow Mg^{2+}(aq) + Cu(s)$

16. $Fe_2O_3(s) + 3\underline{CO}(g) \rightarrow 2Fe(s) + 3CO_2(g)$

17. $Mg(s) + 4\underline{HNO_3}(aq) \rightarrow Mg(NO_3)_2(aq) + 2NO_2(g) + 2H_2O(l)$

18. $2\underline{Na_2S_2O_3}(aq) + I_2(aq) \rightarrow 2NaI(aq) + Na_2S_4O_6(aq)$

Decide whether each of the following

A.   is a redox reaction   **B.**   is **NOT** a redox reaction.

1. $Mg(s)$ + $2H^+(aq)$ → $Mg^{2+}(aq)$ + $H_2(g)$

2. $N_2(g)$ + $3H_2(g)$ → $2NH_3(g)$

3. $H^+(aq)$ + $OH^-(aq)$ → $H_2O(l)$

4. $CuO(s)$ + $CO(g)$ → $Cu(s)$ + $CO_2(g)$

5. $Br_2(aq)$ + $2I^-(aq)$ → $2Br^-(aq)$ + $I_2(aq)$

6. $C_2H_4(g)$ + $H_2(g)$ → $C_2H_6(g)$

7. $Ba^{2+}(aq)$ + $SO_4^{2-}(aq)$ → $BaSO_4(s)$

8. $2Al(s)$ + $3O_2(g)$ → $2Al_2O_3(s)$

9. $Ca(s)$ + $2H_2O(l)$ → $Ca(OH)_2(aq)$ + $H_2(g)$

10. $Cr_2O_7^{2-}(aq)$ + $14H^+(aq)$ + $6I^-(aq)$ → $2Cr^{3+}(aq)$ + $7H_2O(l)$ + $3I_2(aq)$

11. $CuO(s)$ + $2HCl(aq)$ → $CuCl_2(aq)$ + $H_2O(l)$

12. $AgNO_3(aq)$ + $NaCl(aq)$ → $AgCl(s)$ + $NaNO_3(aq)$

13. $SnCl_2(aq)$ + $HgCl_2(aq)$ → $Hg(l)$ + $SnCl_4(aq)$

14. $2Na_2S_2O_3(aq)$ + $I_2(aq)$ → $2NaI(aq)$ + $Na_2S_4O_6(aq)$

15. $2Fe(NO_3)_3(aq)$ + $2KI(aq)$ → $2Fe(NO_3)_2(aq)$ + $2KNO_3(aq)$ + $I_2(aq)$

Test 3.11

Redox titrations

Questions 1 to 5 refer to reactions which occur during redox processes.

Decide the numbers of $H^+(aq)$ and e^- required to balance the ion-election equations.

A. 1   **B.** 2   **C.** 4   **D.** 6   **E.** 10   **F.** 12

1. $SO_3^-(aq)$ $\rightarrow$ $SO_4^{2-}(aq)$

2. XeO_3 $\rightarrow$ Xe

3. ClO^- $\rightarrow$ Cl^-

4. $IO_3^-(aq)$ $\rightarrow$ $I_2(aq)$

5. $PbO_2(s)$ $\rightarrow$ $Pb^{2+}(aq)$

6. The ion-electron equations for a redox reaction are:

$$Fe^{2+}(aq) \rightarrow Fe^{3+}(aq) + e^-$$
$$Cr_2O_7^{2-}(aq) + 14H^+(aq) + 6e^- \rightarrow 2Cr^{3+}(aq) + 7H_2O(l)$$

How many moles of iron(II) ions are oxidised by one mole of dichromate ions?

A. 0.17   **B.** 0.33   **C.** 1   **D.** 6

7. The ion-electron equations for a redox reaction are:

$$2I^-(aq) \rightarrow I_2(aq) + 2e^-$$
$$MnO_4^-(aq) + 8H^+(aq) + 5e^- \rightarrow Mn^{2+}(aq) + 4H_2O(l)$$

How many moles of iodide ions are oxidised by one mole of permanganate ions?

A. 0.2   **B.** 0.4   **C.** 1   **D.** 2.5

8. Dichromate ions react with ethanol in acidic solution.

$$2Cr_2O_7^{2-}(aq) + 3C_2H_5OH(aq) + 16H^+(aq)$$
$$\rightarrow 3CH_3COOH(aq) + 4Cr^{3+}(aq) + 11H_2O(l)$$

How many moles of ethanol are oxidised by one mole of dichromate ions?

A. 1   **B.** 1.5   **C.** 2   **D.** 3

9. Permanganate ions react with hydrogen peroxide in acidic solution.

$$2MnO_4^-{}_{(aq)} + 6H^+{}_{(aq)} + 5H_2O_2{}_{(l)} \rightarrow 2Mn^{2+}{}_{(aq)} + 8H_2O_{(l)} + 5O_2{}_{(g)}$$

How many moles of hydrogen peroxide will react completely with 100 cm^3 of permanganate solution, concentration 0.1 mol l^{-1}?

A. 0.01   **B.** 0.025   **C.** 0.05   **D.** 0.1

10. Iron (II) ions react with dichromate ions in acidic solution.

$$6Fe^{2+}{}_{(aq)} + Cr_2O_7^{2-}{}_{(aq)} + 14H^+{}_{(aq)} \rightarrow 6Fe^{3+}{}_{(aq)} + 2Cr^{3+}{}_{(aq)} + 7H_2O_{(l)}$$

If 25 cm^3 of dichromate solution reacted with 60 cm^3 of iron(II) ion solution, concentration 0.1 mol l^{-1}, calculate the concentration of the dichromate solution, in mol l^{-1}.

A. 0.01   **B.** 0.02   **C.** 0.04   **D.** 0.06

11. The concentration of hydrogen peroxide solution can be found by a redox titration with acidified potassium permanganate solution. The equation for the reaction which takes place is:

$$5H_2O_2{}_{(aq)} + 2MnO_4^-{}_{(aq)} + 6H^+{}_{(aq)} \rightarrow 5O_2{}_{(g)} + 2Mn^{2+}{}_{(aq)} + 8H_2O_{(l)}$$

It was found that 20.0 cm^3 of hydrogen peroxide solution reacted with 40 cm^3 of 0.02 mol l^{-1} potassium permanganate solution when titrated.

Calculate the concentration of the hydrogen peroxide solution, in mol l^{-1}.

A. 0.1   **B.** 0.8   **C.** 2   **D.** 4

12. The chlorine levels in swimming pools can be determined by titrating samples against acidified iron(II) sulphate solution. The reaction taking place is:

$$Cl_2{}_{(aq)} + 2Fe^{2+}{}_{(aq)} \rightarrow 2Cl^-{}_{(aq)} + 2Fe^{3+}{}_{(aq)}$$

A 100 cm^3 sample of water from a swimming pool required 25 cm^3 of iron(II) sulphate concentration 2.0 mol l^{-1}, to reach the end point.

Calculate the chlorine concentration, in g l^{-1}, in the swimming pool water.

A. 0.25   **B.** 17.75   **C.** 35.5   **D.** 71

Questions 1 to 5 refer to the amounts of substances produced during electrolysis.

Decide whether each of the amounts

A. is produced by passage of 96 500 coulombs of electricity
B. is **NOT** produced by passage of 96 500 coulombs of electricity.

1. 1 mol of zinc

2. 0.5 mol of magnesium

3. 2 mol of sodium

4. 1 mol of hydrogen

5. 0.5 mol of iodine

Questions 6 to 10 refer to the quantities of electricity, in coulombs, used during electrolysis.

A.	0.5 x 96 500	**B.**	1 x 96 500
C.	1.5 x 96 500	**D.**	2 x 96 500

What is the quantity of electricity required to produce each of the amounts?

6. 0.5 mol of potassium

7. 1 mol of nickel

8. 0.5 mol of chlorine

9. 0.5 mol of aluminium

10. 0.25 mol oxygen

11. If a steady current of 0.4 A was passed through silver nitrate solution, concentration 1 mol l^{-1}, for 40 minutes, approximately how many moles of silver would be liberated?

A. 0.001   **B.** 0.01   **C.** 0.1   **D.** 1

12. What mass of copper metal, in grams, would be deposited by electrolysis of a solution of Cu^{2+}(aq) ions if 1000 C of electrical charge were passed?

A. 12 352   B. 3.3

C. 0.66   D. 0.33

13. In the electrolysis of a solution of nickel(II) sulphate using nickel electrodes, the passage of 96 500 C of electricity results in the negative electrode

A. gaining 58.7 g mass   B. gaining 29.35 g mass

C. losing 58.7 g mass   D. losing 29.35 g mass.

14. The unlabelled line on the graph was obtained by plotting the mass of copper metal deposited against charge passed during the electrolysis of a solution of copper(I) chloride.

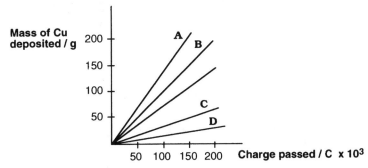

If a solution of copper(II) chloride was electrolysed, which line would be obtained?

15. Silver nitrate solution, concentration 1 mol l^{-1}, is electrolysed. A steady current is maintained until 1.08 g of silver is formed at the negative electrode. The time required to deposit the silver is 30 minutes.

What would be the approximate reading, in amps, on the ammeter?

A. 0.5   B. 1.5

C. 2.0   D. 2.5

16. If 96 500 C of electricity are passed through separate solutons of copper(II) chloride and nickel(II) chloride, then

   A. equal masses of copper and nickel will be deposited
   B. the same number of atoms of each metal will be deposited
   C. the metals will be plated on the positive electrode
   D. different numbes of atoms of each metal will be deposited.

Questions 17 and 18 refer to the electrolysis of solutions of Ag^+(aq) ions and M^{n+}(aq) ions, using the same arrangements as shown.

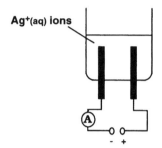
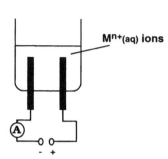

The same quantity of electricity is passed through each solution.

17. If it took 54 hours to deposit 1 mol of Ag, how long would it take to deposit 1 mol of **M**?

   A. 54 **n** hours
   C. 54 / **n** hours
   B. 54 hours
   D. You cannot say without the relative atomic masses of Ag and **M**.

18. If it took 30 minutes to deposit 1 g of Ag, how long would it take to deposit 1 g of **M**?

   A. 30 minutes
   C. 30 / **n** minutes
   B. 30 **n** minutes
   D. You cannot say without the relative atomic masses of Ag and **M**.

1. Isotopes of the same element must have

   A. the same number of protons and neutrons, but different numbers of electrons
   B. the same number of protons and electrons, but different numbers of neutrons
   C. the same number of neutrons, but different numbers of protons and electrons
   D. the same number of protons, but different numbers of electrons and neutrons.

2. Some atoms of an element are heavier than other atoms of the same element.
   This is because they have different numbers of

   A. neutrons **B.** protons **C.** nuclei **D.** electrons.

3. Which of the following statements is **not** true about isotopes?

   A. Their electron arrangements are the same.
   B. The masses of their nuclei are different.
   C. Their numbers of protons are different.
   D. Their nuclear charges are the same.

4. Which statement **cannot** be true of two atoms with the same mass number?

   A. They are isotopes of the same element.
   B. They have different numbers of protons.
   C. They have different numbers of neutrons.
   D. They are atoms of two different elements.

5. The two isotopes of carbon, $^{12}_{6}C$ and $^{14}_{6}C$, differ from each other in

   A. mass number **B.** atomic number
   C. chemical properties **D.** electron arrangement.

6. An isotope of oxygen of mass number 18 differs from the most abundant form of oxygen in

   A. the number of atoms per molecule
   B. the number of electrons in the outer energy level (shell)
   C. the number of protons in each nucleus
   D. the proportion of protons to neutrons in the nucleus.

7. The radioactive isotope of calcium would differ from ordinary (non-active) calcium in its

   A. atomic mass
   B. chemical properties
   C. atomic number
   D. electronic configuration.

   In question 8 to 13 decide whether each of the pairs

   A. are isotopes of the same element
   B. are **NOT** isotopes of the same element.

8. an atom with 6 protons and 8 neutrons
   and
   an atom with 8 protons and 8 neutrons

9. an atom with 10 protons and 10 neutrons
   and
   an atom with 10 protons and 12 neutrons

10. an atom with atomic number 17 and mass number 35
    and
    an atom with atomic number 17 and mass number 37

11. an atom with atomic number 1 and mass number 2
    and
    an atom with atomic number 2 and mass number 4

12. $^{16}_{8}W$ and $^{18}_{8}X$

13. $^{40}_{19}Y$ and $^{40}_{20}Z$

14. Which pair or pairs of atoms are isotopes of the same element?

    $^{86}_{38}W$ $\qquad$ $^{86}_{36}X$ $\qquad$ $^{87}_{38}Y$ $\qquad$ $^{87}_{37}Z$

    A. **W,X** only   B. **W,Y** only
    C. **W,X** and **Y,Z**   D. no pair

15. Information about the atomic structure of atoms is given in the table.

Atom	Number of neutrons in the nucleus	Nuclear charge
1	50	36
2	50	37
3	49	38
4	52	38

Which pair of atoms are isotopes?

A. 1 and 2   **B.** 2 and 3

C. 2 and 4   **D.** 3 and 4

16. An isotope of an element can be represented $^{50}_{24}X$.

Which of the following represents another isotope of the element?

A. $^{50}_{23}X$ **B.** $^{52}_{24}X$ **C.** $^{50}_{25}X$ **D.** $^{52}_{25}X$

Test 3.14

1. The relative atomic mass of an element is rarely a whole number.

   This is because

   A. different atoms of an element can have different numbers of protons
   B. it is difficult to isolate pure elements
   C. chemical methods of determining the relative atomic masses of elements are inaccurate
   D. different atoms of an element can have different numbers of neutrons.

2. An element consists of two isotopes with mass numbers 40 and 42.

   The relative atomic mass must be

   A. 41 exactly
   B. more than 41
   C. less than 41
   D. between 40 and 42, but impossible to specify.

3. Which of the following needs to be known to calculate the relative atomic mass of an element?

   A. the number of protons and the number of neutrons in each isotope
   B. the identities of the isotopes present and their relative abundance
   C. the number of neutrons in each isotope
   D. the number of protons, neutrons and electrons in each isotope

4. The relative atomic mass of lithium is 6.94 amu.

   This is because

   A. all lithium atoms have a mass of 6.94 amu
   B. most lithium atoms have a mass of 7 amu but a few have a mass of 6 amu
   C. most lithium atoms have a mass of 6 amu but a few have a mass of 7 amu
   D. most lithium atoms have a mass of 7 amu but a few have lost an electron.

5. Copper has two isotopes, each with a percentage abundance as shown.

    63Cu   75%   65Cu   25%

    What is the approximate relative atomic mass of copper?

    A.   63   **B.**   63.5   **C.**   64   **D.**   65

6. Naturally occurring gallium (atomic number 31, relative atomic mass 69.7) consists of a mixture of two isotopes of mass numbers 69 and 71.

    Identify the true statement.

    A.   Atoms of gallium 69 are more abundant than those of gallium 71.
    B.   Atoms of the two isotopes of gallium have different numbers of protons.
    C.   Atoms of the two isotopes of gallium have the same number of neutrons.
    D.   All gallium atoms have an atomic mass of 69.7 amu.

7. The relative abundances of the two isotopes of boron are shown in the table.

Isotope	Relative abundance/%
^{10}B	18.7
^{11}B	81.3

    What is the relative atomic mass of boron?

    A.   10   **B.**   10.3   **C.**   10.8   **D.**   11

8. Naturally occurring nitrogen consists of two isotopes ^{14}N and ^{15}N.

    How many types of stable nitrogen moleules will occur in the air?

    A.   1   **B.**   2   **C.**   3   **D.**   4

9. Different isotopes of both hydrogen and oxygen are found in water molecules.

    1   $(^{1}H_2{}^{16}O)$ 2 $(^{1}H_2{}^{17}O)$ 3 $(^{1}H_2{}^{18}O)$

    4   $(^{2}H_2{}^{16}O)$ 5 $(^{2}H_2{}^{17}O)$ 6 $(^{2}H_2{}^{18}O)$

    Which pair of molecules have the same molecular mass?

    A.   1 and 4   **B.**   2 and 5   **C.**   3 and 6   **D.**   3 and 4

Questions 10 and 11 refer to chlorine which has two isotopes, chlorine-35 and chlorine-37.

10. If chlorine molecules are analysed, how many different molecular masses will be detected?

A. 1   **B.** 2   **C.** 3   **D.** 4

11. If chlorine molecules are analysed, which molecular mass will not be found?

A. 70   **B.** 71   **C.** 72   **D.** 74

12. Hydrogen has two main isotopes.

Isotope	Symbol	Mass number	Atomic number
Hydrogen	H	1	1
Deuterium	D	2	1

Which pair of ions have the same molecular mass?

A. H^+ and D^+

B. H_2^+ and D_2^+

C. H_2^+ and D^+

D. H_2^+ and HD^+

13. The chloride of a Group 6 element is analysed.
The element has one isotope and chlorine has two, $^{35}_{17}Cl$ and $^{37}_{17}Cl$.

Molecules are found with mass numbers 180, 182, 184 and 186.

What is the mass number of the element?

A. 75   **B.** 77   **C.** 79   **D.** 81

The questions in this test refer to types of radiation.

A.   alpha radiation   **B.**   beta radiation   **C.**   gamma radiation

1. What name is given to the electrons which are emitted from the nucleus of certain radioactive atoms?

2. What name is given to the particles consisting of 2 protons and 2 neutrons?

3. What name is given to the electromagnetic radiations of a very short wavelength?

4. Which is the most penetrating radiation?

5. Which is the least penetrating radiation?

6. Which radiation is attracted by a positive electric field?

7. Which radiation is attracted by a negative electric field?

8. Which radiation passes through an electric field without deflection?

9. What radiation is represented by $_{-1}^{0}e$?

10. What radiation is represented by $_{2}^{4}He^{2+}$?

11. Which radiation has no mass associated with it?

Test 3.16   Changes in the nucleus

1. The stability of the nucleus of an ion depends on the ratio of

A. mass : charge
B. neutrons : protons
C. neutrons : electrons
D. protons : electrons.

Questions 2 to 6 refer to changes in the nucleus.

	Atomic number	Mass number
A.	increased	no change
B.	decreased	decreased
C.	no change	increased
D.	no change	no change
E.	increased	increased

Describe the change which is associated with each nuclear reaction.

2. beta emission

3. neutron capture

4. alpha emission

5. gamma emission

6. proton capture

7. What is formed when an atom of $^{239}_{92}$U emits a beta particle?

A. $^{240}_{91}$Pa   **B.** $^{239}_{91}$Pa   **C.** $^{239}_{93}$Np   **D.** $^{238}_{92}$U

8. Protactinium-231 is formed by beta emission from a radioisotope of thorium.

What is the mass number of the radioisotope of thorium?

A. 230   **B.** 231   **C.** 232   **D.** 235.

9. What is formed when radium-224 emits an alpha particle?

    A. radon-220   **B.** radon-222
    C. actinium-224   **D.** thorium-228.

10. A radioactive atom of a Group 4 element emits one beta particle.

    The decay product will be an atom of an element in

    A. Group 3   **B.** Group 4
    C. Group 5   **D.** Group 6.

11. An element in Group 4 is formed by alpha emission.

    The radioactive isotope which decays to form the element will be in

    A. Group 2   **B.** Group 3
    C. Group 5   **D.** Group 6.

12. Radioactive $^{14}_{6}C$ decays by beta particle emission.

    Which statement is true of the new nucleus formed?

    A. It has mass number 13.   **B.** It has 6 protons.
    C. It has 7 neutrons.   **D.** It is a carbon nucleus.

    Questions 13 and 14 refer to types of particle involved in nuclear reactions.

    A. an alpha particle   **B.** a beta particle
    C. a proton   **D.** a neutron

    What is the unknown particle in each of the reactions?

13. $^{207}_{82}Pb$ +   ?   → $^{208}_{83}Bi$

14. $^{137}_{56}Ba$ + ^{1}n → $^{138}_{57}La$ +   ?

Questions 15 to 18 refer to processes occurring in nuclear tranformations.

| **A.** | alpha emission | **B.** | proton capture |
| **C.** | beta emission | **D.** | neutron capture |

Which process takes place in each of the transformations?

15. $^{3}_{1}H$ $\rightarrow$ $^{3}_{2}He$

16. $^{23}_{11}Na$ $\rightarrow$ $^{24}_{11}Na$

17. $^{210}_{84}Po$ $\rightarrow$ $^{206}_{82}Pb$

18. $^{207}_{82}Pb$ $\rightarrow$ $^{208}_{83}Bi$

19. When an atom of $^{239}_{92}U$ emits a beta particle, the product formed also decays, emitting another beta particle.

    The atom formed after the second emission is

    A. $^{238}_{88}Ra$ **B.** $^{239}_{90}Th$ **C.** $^{238}_{92}U$ **D.** $^{239}_{94}Pu$.

20. $^{27}_{13}Al$ can absorb an alpha particle with the emission of a neutron.

    What is the product of this reaction?

    A. $^{30}_{14}Si$ **B.** $^{28}_{15}P$ **C.** $^{30}_{15}P$ **D.** $^{31}_{16}S$

21. What is produced when a $^{35}_{17}Cl$ atom captures a neutron and then emits gamma radiation?

    A. $^{36}_{18}Ar$ **B.** $^{36}_{17}Cl$ **C.** $^{35}_{18}Ar$ **D.** $^{31}_{15}P$

22. During neutron bombardment of $^{24}_{12}Mg$, some atoms capture a neutron at the same time emitting a proton.

    What is formed?

    A. $^{23}_{12}Mg$ **B.** $^{23}_{11}Na$ **C.** $^{24}_{11}Na$ **D.** $^{26}_{13}Al$

23. Which series of transformations would produce an atom of the same element as at the start?

    A. alpha,beta,beta
    B. beta,alpha,alpha
    C. alpha,beta,gamma
    D. alpha,beta,neutron capture

24. When $^{27}_{13}Al$ is bombarded by alpha particles, an isotope of phosphorus, $^{30}_{15}P$, is formed and a particle is emitted.

    What is this particle?

    A. a beta particle   **B.** an alpha particle
    C. a proton   **D.** a neutron

25. What sequence of particles is emitted?

    $$^{231}_{91}Pa \quad \rightarrow \quad ^{227}_{89}Ac \quad \rightarrow \quad ^{227}_{90}Th$$

    A. an alpha particle and then a neutron
    B. an alpha particle and then a beta particle
    C. a beta particle and then an alpha particle
    D. a beta particle and then a proton

26. What particle will be formed when an atom of $^{211}_{83}Bi$ loses an alpha particle and the decay product then loses a beta particle?

    A. $^{210}_{79}Au$ **B.** $^{209}_{80}Hg$ **C.** $^{207}_{81}Tl$ **D.** $^{207}_{82}Pb$

27. The following represents part of a natural radioactive decay series.

    $$^{x}U \quad \xrightarrow{\alpha} \quad ^{y}Th \quad \xrightarrow{\beta} \quad ^{231}Pa$$

    Which of the following represent the mass numbers **x** and **y**?

	x	**y**
A.	239	235
B.	232	231
C.	237	233
D.	235	231

Questions 28 to 30 are about induced nuclear reactions. They can be described in a shortened form

T(x, y)P

where the participants are the target nucleus (**T**), the bombarding particle (**x**), the ejected particle (**y**) and the product nucleus (**P**).

Decide whether each of the nuclear reactions

A.   would give the product nucleus suggested

B.   would **not** give the product nucleus suggested.

28. $^{14}_{7}N$ (α,p) $^{17}_{8}O$

29. $^{10}_{5}B$ (α, n) $^{13}_{7}N$

30. $^{236}_{93}Np$ (p, α) $^{238}_{92}U$

Questions 31 to 35 refer to nuclear fission and nuclear fusion.

Decide whether each of the reaction can be classified as

A.   nuclear fission

B.   nuclear fusion

C.   neither

31. $^{2}_{1}H$ + $^{3}_{1}H$ $\rightarrow$ $^{4}_{2}He$ + $^{1}_{0}n$

32. $^{40}_{19}K$ + $^{0}_{-1}e$ $\rightarrow$ $^{40}_{18}Ar$

33. $^{235}_{92}U$ + $^{1}_{0}n$ $\rightarrow$ $^{90}_{38}Sr$ + $^{144}_{54}Xe$ + $2^{1}_{0}n$

34. $^{14}_{7}N$ + $^{1}_{0}n$ $\rightarrow$ $^{14}_{6}C$ + $^{1}_{1}H$

35. $^{12}_{6}C$ + $^{4}_{2}He$ $\rightarrow$ $^{16}_{8}O$

1. When some zinc pellets containing radioactive zinc are placed in a solution of zinc chloride, radioactivity soon appears in the solution.

    Compared to the pellets, the half-life of the radioactive solution will be

    A. shorter   **B.** the same   **C.** longer
    D. dependent upon how long the zinc is in contact with the solution.

2. When some lead pellets containing radioactive lead are placed in a solution of lead nitrate, radioactivity soon appears in the solution.

    Compared to the pellets the solution will show

    A. different intensity of radiation and different half-life
    B. the same intensity of radiation but different half-life
    C. different intensity of radiation but the same half-life
    D. the same intensity of radiation and the same half-life.

3   The half-life of bismuth in 1g of bismuth oxide compared to 1g bismuth sulphate will be

    A. greater because the percentage of bismuth is greater
    B. less because of the greater stability of the smaller oxide ion
    C. the same because the half-life is independent of the percentage of bismuth
    D. impossible to predict.

    Questions 4 and 5 refer to the different masses of two substances containing $^{224}_{88}$Ra, an alpha emitter.

    A. 1 g of radium   **B.** 10 g of radium
    C. 1 g of radium chloride   **D.** 10 g of radium chloride

4. In which substance will the intensity of radiation be least?

5. In which substance will the intensity of radiation be greatest?

6. Radioactive uranium is present in rocks in the form of compounds like uranium(IV) oxide.   When the rock is processed, a large amount of the uranium can be recovered as pure metal.

    Compared to the original rock, the half-life of the pure metal will be

    A. shorter   **B.** the same
    C. longer   **D.** dependent upon the amount
                                        that is recovered.

7. Which of the following processes, if any, would alter the half-life of a sample of radioactive calcium?

   A. cooling it to -50 ⁰C **B.** dissolving it in dilute hydrochloric acid

   C. burning it in air **D.** none of these

Questions 8 and 9 refer to different radioisotopes.

   A. half-life 2.1 years , beta emitter
   B. half-life 1620 years, alpha emitter
   C. half-life 3.92 seconds, alpha emitter
   D. half-life 1.6 minutes, gamma emitter

8. Which radioisotope could be involved in the dating of archaeological objects?

9. Which radioisotope could be used to detect cracks under the surface of a metal pipe?

10. The half-life of tritium, $^3_1$H is 12.4 years. In a bottle of old wine, the $^2_1$H level is found to be $1/16$ th of that in new wine.

    The wine was approximately

    A. 40 years old **B.** 50 years old
    C. 60 years old **D.** 100 years old.

11. $^{24}_{11}$Na is a beta emitter with a half-life of 15 hours.

    What percentage of the original isotope would remain after 45 hours?

    A. 12.5 **B.** 25 **C.** 75 **D.** 87.5

12. ^{14}C has a half-life of 5600 years. An analysis of charcoal from a wood fire shows that its ^{14}C content is 25% that of living wood.

    How many years have passed since the wood for the fire was cut?

    A. 1400 **B.** 4200 **C.** 11 200 **D.** 16 800

13. $^{210}_{84}$Po is an alpha emitter with a half-life of 140 days.

    What percentage of the original isotope would remain after 420 days?

    A. 12.5 **B.** 25 **C.** 75 **D.** 87.5

14. The half-life of the isotope ^{14}C is 5.6×10^3 years.

   What fraction of the original ^{14}C atoms will remain after 2.24×10^4 years?

   A. 0.5   **B.** 0.25   **C.** 0.125   **D.** 0.0625

15. After 48 years the level of radioactivity in a sample of an isotope was found to be $1/8$ th of the level originally.

   What is the half-life of the isotope?

   A. 6 years   **B.** 12 years   **C.** 16 years   **D.** 24 years

16. $^{215}_{81}Tl$ is a beta emitter with a half-life of 4.2 minutes.

   What percentage of the original isotope would remain after 8.4 minutes?

   A. 12.5   **B.** 25   **C.** 50   **D.** 75

17. After 15 days a sample contained 7.5×10^{23} atoms of radioactive bismuth, half-life 5 days.

   How many atoms were in the sample originally?

   A. 2.25×10^{23} **B.** 2.5×10^{23}

   C. 3.75×10^{23} **D.** 6.0×10^{24}

18. $^{210}_{84}Po$ is an alpha emitter with a half-life of 140 days. A sample of the isotope was analysed and the chart shown was obtained.

   What is the age of the isotope?

   A. 140 days
   B. 280 days
   C. 420 days
   D. 840 days

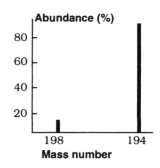

19. The chart shown was obtained from a 12 day old sample of an alpha emitting radioactive isotope.

   What is the half-life of the isotope?

   A. 2 days   **B.** 3 days
   C. 4 days   **D.** 6 days

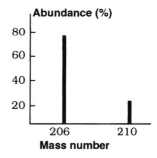

Test 1.1	Test 1.2	Test 1.3	Test 1.4	Test 1.5	Test 1.6
1. A	1. A	1. A	1. A	1. D	1. A
2. A	2. B	2. A	2. B	2. A	2. B
3. B	3. B	3. B	3. A	3. C	3. C
4. A	4. B	4. A	4. A	4. C	4. C
5. B	5. B	5. A	5. A	5. A	5. A
6. A	6. A	6. B	6. B	6. B	6. B
7. B	7. B	7. A	7. A	7. D	7. A
8. A	8. B	8. B	8. B	8. A	8. D
9. C	9. A	9. A	9. C	9. C	9. C
10. B	10. A	10. A		10. C	10. C
11. A	11. B	11. B		11. B	11. A
12. D	12. C	12. A		12. B	12. B
13. C	13. C	13. B		13. C	13. A
14. B	14. A	14. B			14. B
	15. A				15. B
	16. A				16. B
					17. B
					18. A

Test 1.7		Test 1.8	Test 1.9		Test 1.10
1. A	21. B	1. A	1. B	21. B	1. B
2. B	22. D	2. A	2. A	22. B	2. B
3. C	23. D	3. A	3. B	23. B	3. A
4. A	24. D	4. B	4. B	24. C	4. B
5. B	25. B	5. B	5. A	25. A	5. B
6. A	26. C	6. B	6. B	26. C	6. C
7. A	27. C	7. C	7. A	27. C	7. B
8. C	28. D	8. B	8. A	28. B	8. D
9. D	29. D	9. A	9. B	29. C	9. D
10. A		10. B	10. A	30. B	10. B
11. C		11. C	11. B	31. B	11. C
12. B		12. B	12. B	32. B	
13. C		13. A	13. A	33. A	
14. A		14. A	14. A	34. A	
15. A		15. A	15. B	35. A	
16. C		16. A	16. A	36. A	
17. A		17. C	17. A	37. B	
18. B			18. A	38. A	
19. C			19. A	39. B	
20. C			20. B	40. A	

Test 1.11

1. A
2. E
3. A
4. C
5. A
6. B
7. D
8. C
9. A
10. E
11. D
12. C
13. A
14. E
15. D
16. C
17. B
18. A
19. B
20. A
21. C
22. D

Test 1.12

1. B
2. B
3. A
4. A
5. C
6. B
7. A
8. C
9. B
10. A
11. C
12. B
13. C
14. E
15. B
16. C
17. A
18. A
19. B

Test 1.13

1. B
2. B
3. A
4. B
5. A
6. A
7. A
8. B
9. A
10. C
11. B
12. B
13. B
14. C
15. B
16. A
17. C
18. C
19. B
20. A
21. B
22. D
23. B
24. C
25. C
26. B
27. A
28. D
29. A
30. B
31. C
32. D
33. B
34. E
35. C
36. D
37. E
38. A
39. A
40. D

Test 1.14

1. B
2. B
3. A
4. B
5. A
6. B
7. A
8. B
9. B
10. A
11. A
12. A
13. B
14. B
15. C
16. B
17. B
18. D
19. D
20. C
21. B
22. A
23. D
24. A
25. B
26. C
27. C
28. A
29. D
30. B
31. D
32. A
33. C
34. D
35. B
36. A
37. A
38. D

Test 1.15

1. BDE
2. ADG
3. ACE
4. ACF
5. ADE
6. ACG
7. ACG
8. ACG

Test 1.16

1. B
2. B
3. D
4. D
5. D
6. A
7. C
8. C
9. B
10. A
11. D
12. A
13. D

Test 1.17

1. A
2. A
3. A
4. B
5. B
6. C
7. B
8. D
9. B
10. C
11. C
12. C
13. D
14. D
15. C

Test 1.18

1. B
2. A
3. B
4. A
5. A
6. B
7. B
8. A
9. A
10. A
11. B
12. A
13. A
14. B
15. A
16. B
17. A
18. B
19. B
20. B
21. A
22. A
23. B
24. A

Test 1.19

1. B
2. B
3. C
4. A
5. D
6. C
7. B
8. D
9. C
10. C
11. C
12. C
13. A
14. A
15. B

Test 1.20

1. A
2. C
3. D
4. C
5. B
6. D
7. B
8. C
9. B
10. C
11. A
12. B

Test 1.21

1. B
2. A
3. A
4. A
5. B
6. B
7. A
8. A
9. D
10. B
11. A
12. C
13. C
14. A
15. A
16. B
17. B
18. D
19. A
20. D
21. C

Test 1.22

1. C
2. B
3. A
4. B
5. A
6. B
7. B
8. C
9. B
10. B
11. A
12. A
13. B
14. B
15. A
16. B
17. A
18. C
19. C
20. B
21. A
22. A

Test 2.1

1. B
2. B
3. D
4. B
5. C
6. D
7. D
8. D
9. A
10. C

Test 2.2

1. AD
2. AD
3. BE
4. AD
5. BE
6. BE
7. CE
8. BE
9. AD
10. CE
11. BE
12. AD
13. A
14. G
15. C
16. D
17. H
18. J
19. C
20. B
21. B
22. A
23. A
24. C
25. C
26. B
27. C
28. A
29. D
30. D
31. D
32. C
33. A
34. C
35. A
36. B
37. D

Test 2.3

1. A
2. B
3. A
4. B
5. A
6. B
7. A
8. B
9. A
10. A
11. A
12. A
13. B
14. B
15. B
16. B
17. A
18. B
19. A
20. C

Test 2.4

1. E
2. CF
3. G
4. C
5. EF
6. AD
7. E
8. BF
9. B
10. A
11. A
12. A
13. A
14. B
15. A
16. A

Test 2.5

1. CLQU
2. BHW
3. FIMOT
4. ADJPR

Test 2.6

1.	B	21.	A
2.	A	22.	B
3.	B	23.	A
4.	B	24.	B
5.	A	25.	D
6.	B	26.	B
7.	A	27.	C
8.	B	28.	A
9.	B	29.	C
10.	B		
11.	B		
12.	A		
13.	A		
14.	B		
15.	A		
16.	B		
17.	B		
18.	B		
19.	A		
20.	B		

Test 2.7

1.	B
2.	A
3.	A
4.	A
5.	B
6.	A
7.	A
8.	C
9.	D
10.	A
11.	B
12.	A
13.	B
14.	B
15.	A
16.	A
17.	B

Test 2.8

1.	B
2.	B
3.	A
4.	A
5.	B
6.	B
7.	A
8.	A
9.	B
10.	A
11.	B
12.	A
13.	B
14.	A
15.	C
16.	A
17.	B

Test 2.9

1.	B
2.	A
3.	B
4.	A
5.	A
6.	B
7.	A
8.	A
9.	B
10.	A
11.	B
12.	A
13.	B
14.	C
15.	D
16.	A
17.	A
18.	A
19.	B
20.	B
21.	B
22.	B
23.	A

Test 2.10

1.	A
2.	B
3.	A
4.	A
5.	B
6.	A
7.	A
8.	B
9.	B
10.	A
11.	B
12.	A
13.	FH
14.	DFH
15.	B
16.	B
17.	B
18.	C
19.	C
20.	B
21.	A
22.	D
23.	D
24.	B

Test 2.11

1.	B
2.	B
3.	A
4.	C
5.	C
6.	C
7.	B
8.	D
9.	D
10.	C

Test 2.12

1.	CFG LN
2.	AEHI KMO
3.	BDJP

Test 2.13

1.	A
2.	B
3.	A
4.	C
5.	A
6.	C
7.	C
8.	B
9.	A
10.	B
11.	A
12.	B
13.	C
14.	B
15.	A
16.	B
17.	A
18.	B
19.	A
20.	B
21.	A
22.	B
23.	A
24.	B

Test 2.14

1.	B
2.	B
3.	A
4.	B
5.	A
6.	B
7.	C
8.	B
9.	D
10.	A
11.	B
12.	D
13.	A
14.	A
15.	B
16.	B
17.	A
18.	A
19.	A
20.	B

Test 2.15

1.	B
2.	A
3.	B
4.	A
5.	A
6.	B
7.	B
8.	C
9.	D
10.	B
11.	D

Test 2.16

1.	AE
2.	G
3.	D
4.	AB
5.	I
6.	D
7.	H
8.	D
9.	F
10.	AE
11.	D
12.	A
13.	D
14.	I
15.	G
16.	D
17.	C
18.	A
19.	H
20.	AB

Test 2.17		Test 2.18		Test 2.19		Test 2.20		Test 2.21		Test 2.22	
1.	B	1.	B	1.	A	1.	B	1.	A	1.	A
2.	A	2.	A	2.	A	2.	A	2.	D	2.	B
3.	D	3.	A	3.	B	3.	B	3.	E	3.	B
4.	A	4.	D	4.	A	4.	A	4.	C	4.	A
5.	C	5.	A	5.	B	5.	A	5.	B	5.	A
		6.	B	6.	A	6.	D	6.	F	6.	C
		7.	A	7.	B	7.	B	7.	E	7.	A
		8.	B	8.	A	8.	B	8.	A	8.	A
		9.	B	9.	A	9.	A	9.	A	9.	C
		10.	A	10.	B	10.	B	10.	E	10.	C
		11.	B	11.	A	11.	A			11.	B
		12.	A	12.	A	12.	B			12.	A
		13.	B	13.	B	13.	C			13.	C
		14.	A	14.	B	14.	D			14.	A
		15.	B	15.	C	15.	D			15.	C
		16.	A	16.	D					16.	A
		17.	B	17.	A					17.	D
		18.	B	18.	B					18.	B
		19.	C	19.	D					19.	D
		20.	B								
		21.	C								
		22.	A								
		23.	D								
		24.	D								
		25.	B								
		26.	A								

Test 2.23

1.	B
2.	A
3.	D
4.	D
5.	A
6.	A
7.	D
8.	A
9.	B
10.	C
11.	B
12.	B
13.	A
14.	A
15.	D
16.	B
17.	A
18.	A
19.	B
20.	B

Test 3.1	Test 3.2	Test 3.3	Test 3.4	Test 3.5	Test 3.6	
1. A	1. D	1. B	1. A	1. A	1. A	21. D
2. A	2. A	2. A	2. B	2. C	2. B	22. E
3. B	3. A	3. B	3. A	3. C	3. B	23. F
4. A	4. A	4. A	4. B	4. A	4. A	24. D
5. B	5. D	5. B	5. B	5. C	5. A	25. C
6. A	6. C	6. A	6. C	6. C	6. B	26. A
7. B	7. A	7. B	7. A	7. C	7. B	27. C
8. A	8. C	8. A	8. A	8. B	8. B	28. D
9. A	9. A	9. A	9. C	9. C	9. A	29. B
10. B	10. C	10. B	10. A	10. B	10. B	
11. B	11. B	11. B	11. C	11. D	11. A	
12. A	12. D	12. A	12. B	12. A	12. A	
13. A		13. B	13. B	13. C	13. C	
14. B		14. A	14. C	14. C	14. D	
15. B			15. A		15. F	
16. A			16. A		16. E	
17. A			17. B		17. B	
18. B			18. B		18. G	
19. A			19. A		19. H	
20. B					20. A	

Test 3.7	Test 3.8	Test 3.9	Test 3.10	Test 3.11	Test 3.12
1. A	1. B	1. B	1. A	1. BB	1. B
2. C	2. A	2. A	2. B	2. DD	2. A
3. A	3. B	3. A	3. B	3. BB	3. B
4. A	4. B	4. B	4. A	4. FE	4. B
5. C	5. B	5. A	5. A	5. CB	5. A
6. B	6. A	6. A	6. B	6. D	6. A
7. A	7. B	7. A	7. B	7. D	7. D
8. B	8. B	8. B	8. A	8. B	8. B
9. C	9. D	9. A	9. A	9. B	9. C
10. A	10. B	10. B	10. A	10. C	10. B
11. C	11. C	11. A	11. B	11. A	11. B
12. C	12. D	12. B	12. B	12. B	12. D
13. B	13. A	13. B	13. A		13. B
14. C	14. A	14. A	14. A		14. C
15. B	15. C	15. B	15. A		15. A
	16. B	16. A			16. B
	17. B	17. A			17. A
	18. A	18. B			18. D
	19. B				
	20. A				
	21. B				
	22. B				
	23. B				

Test 3.13		Test 3.14		Test 3.15		Test 3.16				Test 3.17	
1.	B	1.	D	1.	B	1.	B	21.	B	1.	B
2.	A	2.	D	2.	A	2.	A	22.	C	2.	C
3.	C	3.	B	3.	C	3.	C	23.	A	3.	C
4.	A	4.	B	4.	C	4.	B	24.	D	4.	C
5.	A	5.	B	5.	A	5.	D	25.	B	5.	B
6.	D	6.	A	6.	B	6.	E	26.	D	6.	B
7.	A	7.	C	7.	A	7.	C	27.	D	7.	D
8.	B	8.	D	8.	C	8.	B	28.	A	8.	B
9.	A	9.	C	9.	B	9.	A	29.	A	9.	D
10.	A	10.	B	10.	A	10.	C	30.	B	10.	B
11.	B	11.	C	11.	C	11.	D	31.	B	11.	A
12.	A	12.	A			12.	C	32.	C	12.	C
13.	B					13.	C	33.	A	13.	A
14.	B					14.	B	34.	C	14.	D
15.	D					15.	C	35.	B	15.	C
16.	B					16.	D			16.	B
						17.	A			17.	D
						18.	B			18.	B
						19.	D			19.	C
						20.	C				